Managing Reality

Book Four

Managing Change

Bronwyn Mitchell and Barry Trebes

Published by Thomas Telford Publishing, Thomas Telford Ltd, 1 Heron Quay, London E14 4JD. URL: www.thomastelford.com

Distributors for Thomas Telford books are
USA: ASCE Press, 1801 Alexander Bell Drive, Reston, VA 20191-4400, USA
Japan: Maruzen Co. Ltd, Book Department, 3–10 Nihonbashi 2-chome, Chuo-ku, Tokyo 103
Australia: DA Books and Journals, 648 Whitehorse Road, Mitcham 3132, Victoria

First published 2005

Also available in this series from Thomas Telford Books
NEC – Managing Reality: Introduction to the Engineering and Construction Contract. ISBN 07277 3392 3
NEC – Managing Reality: Procuring an Engineering and Construction Contract. ISBN 07277 3393 1
NEC – Managing Reality: Managing the contract. ISBN 07277 3394 X
NEC – Managing Reality: Managing procedures. ISBN 07277 3396 6
NEC – Managing Reality: Complete box set. ISBN 07277 3397 4

Also available from Thomas Telford Books
NEC3 (complete box set). ISBN 07277 3382 8

A catalogue record for this book is available from the British Library

9 8 7 6 5 4 3 2 1

ISBN: 0 7277 3395 8

© Thomas Telford Limited 2005

Typeset by Academic + Technical, Bristol
Printed and bound in Great Britain by Bell & Bain Limited, Glasgow, UK

Preface

Now more than a decade on from its initial formal introduction (1st edition 1993), the NEC form of contract remains radical in its ethos and contemporary in its management principles for delivering successful projects in the business environment of 21st century construction. Although conceived in the mid-1980s, in what could be described as a decade of success and excess, with a construction industry racked by conflict and confrontation, the NEC owes much of its current widespread and growing usage to the deep recession of the early 1990s, which forced the construction industry to rethink its approach and performance, as much from a need to survive as from a desire to improve.

It is generally recognised and accepted that Sir Michael Latham's *Constructing the Team*, published in 1994, and Sir John Egan's *Rethinking Construction*, published in 1998, were the two main catalysts and energisers of change and improvement within the construction industry throughout the last decade of the 20th century and into the 21st century. Arguably the NEC was the third key driver of cultural reform and management discipline; indeed the NEC was formally recognised by Latham as being the contract form which, more than any other, aligned to his vision for future construction and Egan similarly embraced the NEC as part of his movement for innovation.

Usage has brought with it practical experience and accordingly the thrust of this book is about dealing with the reality of real-life projects. The authors have a combined knowledge and hands-on experience of NEC-managed projects spanning some 20 years and have therefore written the book with the specific purpose of advising and assisting those who would wish to use or even those who already do use the ECC, on the concepts of modern contract practices, procedures and administration.

This book is about 'how to': how to manage the ECC contract and how to administer it. As such, it does not attempt to give a legal treatise or a blow-by-blow review of each and every clause and certainly is not a rehash of the NEC/ECC Guidance Notes. It is intended to be complementary to other publications, which give excellent theoretical and legal perspectives. This book is about managing reality.

Although now regarded as a 'mature' form of contract the ECC is still relatively young when compared to more traditional forms. Therefore, even with current practitioners, experience will vary both in duration and depth. With this in mind the book has been consciously structured so as to be presented as a five-part book-set that covers the needs of the student professional or prospective client, through to the novice practitioner and experienced user. It provides a rounded view of the ECC, whatever your discipline, on both sides of the contractual relationship and is aimed at enabling everyone to realise the business benefits from using the NEC suite of contracts generally and the ECC in particular.

Since the NEC's official launch in 1993, adoption and usage of the NEC, renamed *Engineering and Construction Contract – ECC* in 1995 (2nd edition), has grown, such that it is now the most frequently used contract form for civils, transportation infrastructure and utilities works and is increasingly the preferred form for building construction projects. The latest edition of the contract (NEC3) was issued in July 2005.

The wide acceptance of the NEC generally and its elevation in stature as the preferred contract form is further reinforced by the Office of Government Commerce's endorsement of the third edition (NEC3). These five books take account of the changes introduced to the contract within NEC3.

Foreword

As almost the first UK client to use the NEC, even in its consultative form prior to its launch in 1993, I believe *NEC: Managing Reality* to be a welcome addition to the construction bookshelf: an essential introduction to the NEC for the prospective 'novice' practitioner and an excellent *aide-mémoire* reference book for the regular user of this form of contract.

The joy of this new book is that it brings together a wealth of practical expertise and knowledge from two of the UK's most experienced NEC practitioners written in a style that keeps faith with NEC principles of clarity and simplicity, while respecting differing levels of knowledge within its potential readership.

I have always believed that choosing the contract form is as much a business issue as a construction decision and that business success only results from good management. Certainly this book gives emphasis to the ethos of managing for success rather than the reactive debate of failure. It imparts knowledge, understanding and practical experience of the Contract in use and equally stresses the roles, responsibilities and discipline of the management procedures that apply to everyone. I particularly like the five-module format, in that it presents itself in readable, manageable chunks that can be readily digested or revisited whatever the reader's previous experience of its use.

This book educates, giving guidance and confidence to anyone dealing with real contract issues, following both the spirit as well as the letter of the Contract. It is arguably the most comprehensive practical treatise to date on how to manage and administer the ECC. It is a must for the professional office. Every 'home' should have one.

David H Williams, CEng, FICE
Chairman, Needlemans

(Formerly Group Construction and Engineering Director BAA plc;
founding Chairman, NEC UK Users Group: 1994–1997)

Introduction

General

This series of books will provide the people who are actually using the Engineering and Construction Contract (ECC) in particular, and the New Engineering Contract (NEC) suite in general, practical guidance as to how to prepare and manage an ECC contract with confidence and knowledge of the effects of their actions on the Contract and the other parties.

Each book in the series addresses a different area of the management of an ECC contract.

- Book One – NEC Managing Reality: Introduction to the Engineering and Construction Contract
- Book Two – NEC Managing Reality: Procuring an Engineering and Construction Contract
- Book Three – NEC Managing Reality: Managing the Contract
- Book Four – NEC Managing Reality: Managing Change
- Book Five – NEC Managing Reality: Managing Procedures

- *Book One (NEC Managing Reality: Introduction to the Engineering and Construction Contract)* is for those who are considering using the ECC but need further information, or those who are already using the ECC but need further insight into its rationale. It therefore focuses on the fundamental cultural changes and mind-shift that is required to successfully manage the practicalities of the ECC in use.

- *Book Two (NEC Managing Reality: Procuring an Engineering and Construction Contract)* is for those who need to know how to procure an ECC contract. It covers in practical detail the invitations to tender, evaluation of submissions, which option to select, how to complete the Contract Data and how to prepare the Works Information. The use of this guidance is appropriate for employers, contractors (including subcontractors) and construction professionals generally.

- *Book Three (NEC Managing Reality: Managing the Contract)* is essentially for those who use the contract on a daily basis, covering the detail of practical management such as paying the contractor, reviewing the programme, ensuring the quality of the works and dispute resolution. Both first-time and experienced practitioners will benefit from this book.

- *Book Four (NEC Managing Reality: Managing Change)* is for those who are managing change under the contract; whether for the employer or the contractor (or subcontractor) the management of change is often a major challenge whatever the form of contract. The ECC deals with change in a different way to other more traditional forms. This book sets out the steps to efficiently and effectively manage change, bridging the gap between theory and practice.

- *Book Five (NEC Managing Reality: Managing Procedures)* gives step-by-step guidance on how to apply the most commonly used procedures, detailing the actions needed by all parties to comply with the contract. Anyone administering the contract will benefit from this book.

Background

The ECC is the first of what could be termed a 'modern contract' in that it seeks to holistically align the setting up of a contract to match business needs as opposed to writing a contract that merely administers construction events.

The whole ethos of the ECC, or indeed the NEC suite generally, is one of simplicity of language and clarity of requirement. It is important that the roles and responsibilities are equally clear in definition and ownership.

When looking at the ECC for the first time it is very easy to believe that it is relatively straightforward and simple. However, this apparent simplicity belies the need for the people involved to think about their project and their role and how the ECC can deliver their particular contract strategy.

The ECC provides a structured flexible framework for setting up an appropriate form of contract whatever the selected procurement route. The fundamental requirements are as follows.

- The Works Information – quality and completeness – what are you asking the Contractor to do?
- The Site Information – what are the site conditions the Contractor will find?
- The Contract Data – key objectives for completion, for example start date, completion date, programme – when do you want it completed?

The details contained in the series of books will underline the relevance and importance of the above three fundamental requirements.

The structure of the books

Each chapter starts with a synopsis of what is included in that chapter. Throughout the book there are shaded 'practical tip' boxes that immediately point the user towards important reminders for using the ECC (see example below).

> Clarity and completeness of the Works Information is fundamental.

There are also unshaded boxes that include examples to illustrate the text (see example below).

> Imagine a situation in which the *Supervisor* notifies the *Contractor* that the reinstatement of carriageways on a utility diversion project is not to the highway authority's usual standards. However, the Works Information is silent about the reinstatement.
>
> Although it is not to the authority's usual standard, it is **not** a Defect because the test of a Defect is non-conformance with the Works Information. In this situation, if the *works* need to be redone to meet the authority's requirements, the *Contractor* is entitled to a compensation event because the new requirements are a change to the Works Information.

Other diagrams and tables are designed to maintain interest and provide another medium of explanation. There are also standard forms for use in the administration and management of the contract together with examples.

Throughout the books, the following terms have been used in a specific way.

- NEC is the abbreviation for the suite of New Engineering Contracts and it is not the name of any single contract.
- ECC is the abbreviation for the contract in the NEC suite called the Engineering and Construction Contract.

The NEC suite currently comprises the

- Engineering and Construction Contract
- Engineering and Construction Subcontract

- Engineering and Construction Short Contract
- Engineering and Construction Short Subcontract
- Professional Services Contract
- Adjudicator's Contract
- Term Service Contract
- Framework Contract

Acknowledgements

We would like to thank the following individuals and companies who have supported the book.

Andy Door who gave advice on procurement within the public sector. Mike Attridge of Ellenbrook Consulting who reviewed the book on behalf of the authors. David H. Williams who provided guidance and support in the development of the book and everyone at Needlemans Construction Consultants and MPS Limited.

                                   www.neccontract.com

Series Contents

The following outlines the content of the five books in the series.

Book 1 NEC Managing Reality: Introduction to the Engineering and Construction Contract

Preface, Foreword, Introduction and Acknowledgements
Series Contents, Contents, List of tables, List of figures

Chapter 1 Introduction to the Engineering and Construction Contract, concepts and terminology

Synopsis
This chapter looks at:

- An introduction to the ECC
- An identification of some of the differences between the ECC and other contracts
- A brief outline of differences between ECC2 and ECC3
- An outline of the key features of the ECC
- Conventions of the ECC
- Concepts on which the ECC is based
- Terminology used in the ECC
- Terminology not used in the ECC
- How the ECC affects the way you work

Appendix 1 Summary of differences between ECC2 and ECC3

Chapter 2 Roles in the Engineering and Construction Contract

Synopsis
This chapter describes the roles adopted in the ECC including:

- How to designate a role
- Discussion of the roles described in the ECC
- Discussion of the project team
- How the ECC affects each of the roles

Appendix 2 List of duties

Book 2 NEC Managing Reality: Procuring an Engineering and Construction Contract

Preface, Foreword, Introduction and Acknowledgements
Series Contents, Contents, List of tables, List of figures

Chapter 1 Procurement

Synopsis
This chapter looks at the concept of procurement and contracting strategies and discusses:

- Procurement and contract strategy
- What tender documents to include in an ECC invitation to tender
- How to draft and compile a contract using the ECC
- Procurement scenarios that an employer could face and how to approach them

- The terminology used to describe the programme
- What the programme is
- The definition and purpose of the Accepted Programme
- How and when to submit programmes
- What the programme is used for
- What to include in the programme

Chapter 3   Control of quality

Synopsis
This chapter discusses:

- The quality framework embedded within the ECC
- The *Contractor*'s obligations
- Role of the *Employer*'s representatives
- Subcontracting
- Quality control

Chapter 4   Disputes and dispute resolution

Synopsis
This chapter:

- Emphasises the importance of early dispute resolution to the successful outcome of a contract
- Considers the common sources of dispute
- Considers how the ECC has been designed to reduce the incidence of disputes
- Examines how the ECC provides for the resolution of disputes
- Looks at the implications for the dispute resolution process as a result of the new Housing Grants, Construction and Regeneration Act 1996
- Looks at ECC3 changes in relation to adjudication.

Book 4   NEC Managing Reality: Managing Change

Preface, Foreword, Introduction and Acknowledgements
Series Contents, Contents, List of tables, List of figures

Chapter 1   Compensation Events

Synopsis
This chapter describes the following:

- The compensation events contained within the ECC
- Procedure for administering compensation events
- Roles played by the two main parties to the contract in relation to compensation events

Appendix 1   Compensation event procedures

Chapter 2   Schedule of Cost Components

Synopsis
This chapter discusses aspects relating to the Schedule of Cost Components including:

- When the Schedule of Cost Components is used
- How the SCC interacts with the payment clauses
- Actual Cost and Defined Cost
- The Fee
- The components of cost included under the Schedule of Cost Components
- Contract Data part two

Appendix 2   Section A: ECC2 example quotations
Section B: ECC3 example quotations
Appendix 3   Example people costs
Appendix 4   Preliminaries comparison
Appendix 5   *Contractor*'s and Subcontractor's share example

Book 5 NEC Managing Reality: Managing Procedures

Preface, Foreword, Introduction and Acknowledgements
Series Contents, Contents, List of tables, List of figures

Chapter 1 ECC Management: Procedures

Synopsis
This chapter brings together all the aspects discussed in previous chapters in
Books 1 to 4, which form part of the series of books on NEC Managing Reality.
This chapter provides the 'how to' part of the series. It introduces some
example pro-formas for use on the contract.

For quick reference, this chapter may be read on its own. It does not, however,
detail the reasons for carrying out the actions, or the clause numbers that
should be referred to in order to verify the actions in accordance with the
contract. These are described in detail in other chapters that form part of this
series.

Contents

List of tables

List of figures

1 Compensation events

© copyright nec 2005

Synopsis

This chapter describes the following:

- The compensation events contained within the ECC

- Procedure for administering compensation events

- Roles played by the two main parties to the contract in relation to compensation events

1.1 Introduction

One of the underlying principles of the ECC is to avoid and reduce the amount of change that occurs on construction projects. However, the contract recognises that change is inevitable even when the project has been well planned and prepared and it sets out to deal with the effects and consequences of change in an improved way.

The contract recognises that the earlier an event which could affect the cost, time or quality of a project is identified, then the more likely it is that its effects can be reduced or even avoided. The ECC early warning procedure is what it says: an early warning mechanism for change. Should the change become necessary, then the contract tries to deal with the effects of change in an improved way by use of quotations for compensation events.

Compensation events represent the mechanism for the *Contractor*, ensuring that he is not out of pocket for things that happen that are outwith his control. Unlike some traditional contracts, which address 'extensions of time' and 'variations' separately, the ECC regards changes as a package of time and money. This means that for every event the effects on both the programme (the Completion Date[1]) and the contract sum (the total of the Prices) are considered at the same time.

Apart from a clear and finite list of events that could trigger a compensation event, other points to note are that:

- the *Contractor* can notify a compensation event if it is less than two weeks since he became aware of it,[2]
- inclement weather is not confined to an extension of time assessment,
- physical conditions, such as ground conditions, rely on information provided by the *Employer*,
- the procedure for most compensation events takes place within a maximum time period of eight weeks.

> Compensation events are events which are at the *employers* risk in the contract.

1.2 Compensation event procedure: background

In order to understand why the compensation event procedure has developed into the form found in the ECC, it is necessary to consider some of the principles upon which the contract is founded.

Every procedure has been designed so that its implementation should contribute to, rather than detract from, the effectiveness of the management of the work. In this context, management includes cost and time management.

The ECC is based on the principle that foresight applied collaboratively mitigates problems and shrinks risk. This could be considered a departure from traditional contracts which tend to view the Engineer/Architect/Supervising Officer as the font of all knowledge, paying little or no regard to any worthwhile contribution the *Contractor* may have to offer in the area of problem resolution. Latham acknowledged this issue in *Constructing the Team* when advocating that a modern form of contract should include 'firm duties of teamwork with shared financial motivation to pursue the teamwork approach. These should involve a general presumption to achieve "win–win" solutions to problems which may arise during the course of a project.' Continuing on this theme, the ECC motivates people to play their part in collaborative management if it is in their commercial (*Employer* and *Contractor*) and professional (consultants, e.g. designers, *Project Managers*) interest to do so.

---

[1] And Key Dates in ECC3.
[2] ECC3 clause 61.3 bars the *Contractor* from notifying a compensation event more than eight weeks after he became aware of the event, except in specific circumstances.

The ECC sets out to motivate these people by clearly defining the actions to be taken, clearly stating who is responsible for taking those actions, and giving periods within which the actions are required to be taken. Such is the emphasis the ECC places on collaborative management that sanctions exist within the contract to be applied to the party who does not play his part. These sanctions take the form of financial penalties (direct and indirect) for such lapses as failure to reply within the *period for reply*, failure to give early warnings, failure to keep the programme up to date and failure to submit quotations on time.

Another principle to assist with the efficient management of the *works* is that the *Project Manager*, acting on behalf of the *Employer* and in communication with him, should be presented with options for dealing with a 'problem'. The *Contractor* should be indifferent to the choice made in terms of time and money.

This is achieved by basing the valuation of compensation events on a forecast of their impact upon the cost to the *Contractor* of carrying out the *works* as forecast by him at the time the event is assessed. Where, as is often the case, alternative ways of dealing with the 'problem' are possible, the *Contractor* prepares quotations for different ways of tackling the 'problem'.[3] The *Project Manager* selects one on the basis of which will serve the best interests of the *Employer*. In some cases this will be the lowest cost solution, in others it might be the least delay solution, or a combination of factors.

The financial effects of a compensation event are based upon a quotation prepared by the *Contractor* and preferably in advance of the work (the subject of the compensation event) being carried out. Under price-based contracts (Options A and B), the *Contractor* carries the risk if his forecast of financial effect turns out to be wrong and consequently the *Employer* has a firm commitment. Under the target cost contracts (Options A and B), the *Contractor* carries some risk if his forecast is wrong, as it will affect his final 'share' from the target mechanism. This is justified on the grounds that:

- it stimulates foresight in that it enables the *Employer* to make rational decisions about changes to the work with reasonable certainty of their cost and time implications and
- at the same time, puts a risk on the *Contractor* which motivates him to manage the new situation efficiently.

An important by-product of the procedure included in the ECC for compensation events is that few, if any, issues relating to the valuation of work or extensions of time are left to be settled after the event.

> The compensation event procedure is a quick procedure designed to value change during the period of the contract and not after Completion.

1.3 What is a compensation event?

Compensation events are events that are at the *Employer*'s risk under the Contract and that entitle the *Contractor* to an assessment of the effect the event has on the Prices and the Completion Date.[4] Risks that are not specifically identified as being the *Employer*'s are at the *Contractor*'s risk.[5] The *Contractor* should therefore be aware of the events that are likely to arise and will be at his risk under the contract. These items should be considered in the carrying out of his risk assessment prior to the *starting date*.[6]

The assessment of a compensation event is always of its effect on both the Prices and the Completion Date.[7] In other words, there are not separate clauses for events that result in an 'extension of time' and for events that

---

[3]See clause 62.1. ECC3 requires the practicable options to be discussed with the *Contractor*.
[4]ECC3 includes the Key Date.
[5]Clause 81.1.
[6]ECC3 includes for matters to be listed in a Risk Register in both Contract Data parts one and two.
[7]ECC3 includes Key Date.

---

result in changes to the Prices. For all events, the effect on both the Prices and the programme are always considered together. This does not mean that every event will always have an effect on both time and the Prices, but this effect has to be assessed in order to reach such a conclusion. In the case of some events, the assessment may be reduced payments to the *Contractor*.

> Compensation events consider the effect on both time and money.

A compensation event is a different name for various terms that do not apply in the ECC and should not be referred to as:

- variations,
- extension of time,
- loss and expense,
- delay and disruption,
- claim.

1.4 Where to find a list of compensation events

Compensation events can be found in four places:

(1)   Clause 60.1 lists 18 compensation events.[8]
(2)   Main Options B and D include additional compensation events in clauses 60.4, 60.5 and 60.6, which relate to the use of *bills of quantities*.[9]
(3)   Secondary Options J, T, U and Y(UK)2 (and X15 in ECC3) include compensation events.[10]
(4)   The *Employer* has the option of inserting additional compensation events in Contract Data part one.

A compensation event is much more than scope changes. A change in scope is covered by only one of the 18-plus compensation events that are listed.[11]

1.4.1 Core compensation events   A discussion of the compensation events listed under Clause 60.1 of the ECC is given below.

Compensation event 60.1(1)

'60.1(1)   The *Project Manager* gives an instruction changing the Works Information except:
- a change made in order to accept a Defect or
- a change to the Works Information provided by the *Contractor* for his design, which is made [ECC3 either] at his request or to comply with other Works Information provided by the *Employer*.'

This clause is simply the result of an instruction given by the *Project Manager* varying the *works*, for example deletion or addition of work, change to specifications, issue of a revised drawing, clarification of verbal instruction. Any instruction to change the *works* as a result of clause 17.1 (ambiguities and inconsistencies) or 19.1 (illegal and impossible requirements)[12] will also fall under this compensation event.

The two bullet points in clause 60.1(1) detail the two exceptions to a change to the Works Information being a compensation event.

(1)   The *Project Manager* may agree, for reasons of efficacy, to accept a Defect created by the *Contractor*.[13] If so, then he would instruct a

[8]ECC3 introduces a new clause 60.1(19) – introduced because of the issues raised during the foot-and-mouth epidemic where acts of God outside the control of either party were not adequately dealt with in the contract.
[9]ECC3 introduces a new clause 60.7, which outlines that the *Contractor* is deemed to have taken the Bill of Quantities as being correct when assessing a compensation event.
[10]ECC3 secondary Options X2 (NEC2 Option T), Option X14 (NEC2 Option J), ECC2 Option U deleted.
[11]ECC3 19 compensation events.
[12]ECC3 renumbered to 18.1.
[13]Clause 44 of the ECC and discussed further in Chapter 3 of Book 3.

change to the Works Information after acceptance of the *Contractor's* quotation under clause 44.2. The resulting change to the Works Information to ensure that the Works Information reflects the *works* as built (including Defect) is not regarded as a compensation event.

(2) Where the *Contractor* has designed the *works*, and/or has included Works Information as part of his proposal, there will be two parts to the Works Information that form part of the contract: Works Information by the *Employer*; and Works Information by the *Contractor*. Although the Works Information by the *Contractor* forms part of the Works Information, the *Contractor* retains ownership of it and any changes to it made at the request of the *Contractor* or to ensure that it complies to the Works Information by the *Employer* are not construed as changes to the Works Information provided by the *Employer*. To avoid confusion, a *Project Manager* instructing a change to the *Contractor's* Works Information should make it clear in the instruction that the change is not to the *Employer's* Works Information, but is a change to the *Contractor's* Works Information either (tick as appropriate) made at the *Contractor's* request or to comply with Works Information by the *Employer*.

Compensation event 60.1(2)

ECC2: '60.1(2)   The *Employer* does not give possession of a part of the Site by the later of its *possession date* and the date required by the Accepted Programme.'

ECC3: '60.1(2)   The *Employer* does not allow access to and use of a part of the Site by the later of its *access date* and the date shown on the Accepted Programme.'

The *Employer* will have included *possession dates* [ECC3 *access dates*] in Contract Data part one; that is, dates by which the *Employer* intends to give the *Contractor* possession [ECC3 access] of the Site or parts of it. The *Contractor* will have included in his programme submitted for acceptance the date by which he requires possession/access of the Site or parts of it. These latter dates included by the *Contractor* in his programme may be later than the *possession/access dates* proposed by the *Employer*. Clause 33.1 of the ECC clearly states the obligations of the *Employer* in giving possession/access of the Site to the *Contractor*; that is, to give possession/access by the later of the *possession/access date* stated in Contract Data part one or the date for possession/access given on the Accepted Programme.[14] If the *Employer* fails in this obligation, it is a compensation event.

Compensation event 60.1(3)

ECC2: '60.1(3)   The *Employer* does not provide something which he is to provide by the date for providing it required by the Accepted Programme.'

ECC3: '60.1(3)   The words "required by" are deleted and replaced with "shown on".'

The change in wording is to make it clear that where a *Contractor* requires the *Employer* to provide something, that this is shown on the Accepted Programme and not lost in supporting information as it could be in ECC2.

The Works Information should state clearly details of anything, such as Plant and Materials or facilities, which the *Employer* is to provide and any restrictions on when it is to be provided. Clause 31.2 requires the *Contractor* to include this information in his Accepted Programme. If the *Employer* fails to provide this information by the relevant date, the *Contractor* is entitled to notify the event as a compensation event. Note that this compensation event depends on the *Contractor* having entered the dates on his programme.

Compensation event 60.1(4)

ECC2: '60.1(4)   The *Project Manager* gives an instruction to stop or not to start any work.'

[14]This is discussed further in Chapter 2 of Book 3.

ECC3: '60.1(4) The *Project Manager* gives an instruction to stop or not to start any work or to change a Key Date.'

Clause 34.1 of the ECC gives the *Project Manager* the authority to instruct the *Contractor* to stop or not to start work. One of the many reasons the *Project Manager* may give such an instruction is for reasons of safety. Such an instruction is a compensation event. Some employers change this clause using a secondary Option Z clause to add that where the instruction relates to health and safety matters or is in relation to a *Contractor* default, the instruction is not a compensation event. Clause 14.3 (ECC3) gives the *Project Manager* the authority to instruct the *Contractor* to change a Key Date.

Compensation event 60.1(5)

ECC2: '60.1(5) The *Employer* or Others do not work within the times shown on the Accepted Programme or do not work within the conditions stated in the Works Information.'

ECC3: '60.1(5) New third bullet point added:
"carry out work on the Site that is not stated in the Works Information".'

The Works Information should state clearly details of the order and timing of work to be done by the *Employer* and Others. Clause 31.2 requires the *Contractor* to include this information on his Accepted Programme. If the *Employer* or Others work outside these parameters, it is a compensation event. Note that this compensation event depends on the *Contractor* having entered the dates on his programme.

Compensation event 60.1(6)

'60.1(6) The *Project Manager* or the *Supervisor* does not reply to a communication from the *Contractor* within the period required by this contract.'

Certain clauses within the ECC give various periods for reply by the *Project Manager* and *Supervisor*. A default *period for reply* is given in part one of the Contract Data and the obligation to reply within the relevant period is given in clause 13.3. Where communication is not made within the time-scales given, the *Contractor* may notify a compensation event. Note that any time period may be extended by agreement between the *Project Manager* and the *Contractor*.

Compensation event 60.1(7)

'60.1(7) The *Project Manager* gives an instruction for dealing with an object of value or of historical or other interest found within the Site.'

Clause 73.1 of the ECC states the procedure for dealing with such items. Any instruction for dealing with an object of value or of historical or other interest found within the Site would be additional work for the *Contractor* and therefore a compensation event.

Compensation event 60.1(8)

'60.1(8) The *Project Manager* or the *Supervisor* changes a decision which he has previously communicated to the *Contractor*.'

Both the *Project Manager* and the *Supervisor* are able to change decisions made under the authority given to them under the ECC. Any such changed decision is likely to result in extra work for the *Contractor* and would therefore be a compensation event.

Compensation event 60.1(9)

'60.1(9) The *Project Manager* withholds an acceptance (other than acceptance of a quotation for acceleration or for not correcting a Defect) for a reason not stated in this contract.'

There are various clauses in the ECC that state reasons why the *Project Manager* is entitled not to accept a submission or proposal from the *Contractor*. Examples are clauses 24.1 (people) and 31.3 (the programme). Where the

Project Manager does not accept a submission from the *Contractor* and the reason he states is not one of the reasons allowed by the ECC then the *Contractor* may notify a compensation event. If the withheld acceptance is for a quotation for acceleration[15] or for acceptance of a Defect,[16] then the non-acceptance is not a compensation event. This is because both the quotation for acceleration and the quotation for accepting a Defect are voluntary.

Compensation event 60.1(10)

'60.1(10)   The *Supervisor* instructs the *Contractor* to search [ECC3 the words 'for a Defect' are inserted here] and no Defect is found unless the search is needed only because the *Contractor* gave insufficient notice of doing work obstructing a required test or inspection.'

Clause 42.1 of the ECC allows the *Supervisor* to instruct the *Contractor* to search.[17] Since a search that does not reveal a Defect would have been unfair to the *Contractor*, a compensation event allows him to notify the time and cost that the unnecessary search has resulted in. If, however, the search was required because the *Contractor* did not give sufficient notice for the test or inspection,[18] then any search is not a compensation event, whether or not a Defect is found.

Compensation event 60.1(11)

'60.1(11)   A test or inspection done by the *Supervisor* causes unnecessary delay.'

The Works Information should state clearly those tests or inspections that are to be carried out by the *Supervisor* and the *Contractor*, whether witnessed by the *Supervisor* or not. Clause 40.5 of the ECC requires the *Supervisor* to carry out his tests and inspections without causing unnecessary delay. Although the word 'unnecessary' could be a little vague, the *Contractor* could evidence the delay through using his programme for the commencement date of following activities.

Compensation event 60.1(12)

ECC2: '60.1(12)   The *Contractor* encounters physical conditions which

- are within the Site
- are not weather conditions and
- which [ECC3 'which' is deleted] an experienced contractor would have judged at the Contract Date to have such a small chance of occurring that it would have been unreasonable for him to have allowed for them.'

ECC3: '60.1(12)   New paragraph added:
"Only the difference between the physical conditions encountered and those for which it would have been reasonable to have allowed is taken into account in assessing a compensation event".'

In ECC2 it was contended by some that if a compensation event occurred under this clause then the *Contractor* was entitled to the full effect of the event. The additional wording clarifies that the *Contractor*'s entitlement is limited to the event's effect over and above to that which 'would have been reasonable to have allowed'.

This compensation event means that the *Employer* takes the risk for physical conditions. Note that 'physical conditions' includes more than just ground conditions. A statement in the instructions to tenderers that 'the tenderer shall make whatever arrangements are necessary to become fully informed regarding all existing and expected conditions and matters which might in any way affect the cost of the performance of the *works* and claims for additional reimbursement on the grounds of lack of knowledge or failure to fully investigate

---

[15]Clause 36.
[16]Clause 44.
[17]ECC3: the words 'Until the *defects date* ...' have been added to the beginning of the clause.
[18]Clause 40.3.

the foregoing conditions shall not relieve the tenderer from the responsibility for estimating properly the difficulty or cost of successfully performing any work' does not relieve the *Employer* of his responsibilities.

As with the integration of the early warning clause into a compensation event,[19] clause 60.1(12) refers to an 'experienced' contractor.

Clause 60.1(12) is read with clause 60.2 and clause 60.3.[20] Clause 60.2 describes the aspects of the physical conditions[21] that the *Contractor* is assumed to have taken into account when judging (at the Contract Date) whether they had such a small chance of occurring that it would have been unreasonable to have allowed for them. This means that it is in the *Employer*'s interests to provide as much information to the *Contractor* as possible, in order to discharge his own duties.

Clause 60.3 states the 'contra proferentem' rule regarding inconsistencies (ECC3; and ambiguities) in the Site Information, for which the *Employer* is responsible.

This compensation event is the standard ground conditions variation that has been with the construction industry for many years. It is important when preparing the tender documentation under an ECC that the following points are borne in mind:

- The more information concerning ground conditions that can be provided, the greater the certainty with which appropriate allowances can be made by the tenderers.
- It is important that the information provided is both correct and relevant to the risks faced.
- It may be useful for the *Employer* to utilise a specialist to provide interpretation of factual data to ensure tenders are on a common basis.
- The *Employer* may utilise the works information or secondary Option Z whereby he can define in the contract the limit between the risks carried by the *Employer* and the *Contractor*; that is, to indicate what should be allowed for in the Prices. An example of such limits would be for the *Employer* to state the limits for groundwater levels.

If an *Employer* chooses to delete clause 60.1(12), using Option Z, then **all** the risks for physical conditions are taken by the *Contractor*, not only those that he has misjudged, given the information provided by the *Employer*. Perhaps the *Employer* should consider why the *Contractor* should take the risk of physical conditions if the *Employer* is not prepared to, even though the *Employer* is more likely to have the information regarding the physical conditions.

> Deleting compensation events 60.1(12) and 60.1(13) means more than simply deleting those clauses. It is also worth considering whether the *Contractor* can manage those risks better than the *Employer*.

Compensation event 60.1(13)

ECC2: '60.1(13)   A *weather measurement* is recorded:

- within a calendar month
- before the Completion Date for the whole of the works and
- at the place stated in the Contract Data

the value of which, by comparison with the *weather data*, is shown to occur on average less frequently than once in ten years.'

ECC3: '60.1(13)   New paragraph added:

"Only the difference between the *weather measurement* and the weather which the *weather data* show to occur on average more frequently than

[19]Clause 61.5.
[20]In ECC3 clause 60.3 the word 'ambiguity' has been added.
[21]Note that the compensation event refers to physical conditions and not simply ground conditions, where physical conditions has a much wider connotation.

once in ten years is taken into account in assessing a compensation event".'

In ECC2 it was contended by some that if a compensation event occurred under this clause then the *Contractor* was entitled to the full effect of the event. The additional wording clarifies that the *Contractor*'s entitlement is limited to the difference between the *weather data* and the *weather measurement.*

The ECC does not refer to 'inclement' weather, but rather weather that occurs on average less frequently than once in ten years, using a defined set of records, possibly those available from the Met office.[22] This is a more objective and measurable approach than other standard forms of contract.

The purpose is to make available for each contract *weather data*, compiled by an independent authority[23] and agreed by both Parties beforehand, establishing the levels of selected relevant weather conditions for the Site for each calendar month which have had a period of return of more than ten years. If weather conditions more adverse than these levels occur, it is a compensation event. Weather, which the *weather data* show is likely to occur less frequently than once within a ten-year period, is the *Contractor*'s risk in relation to both cost and time.

The time of occurrence of all compensation events is when the action or lack of action describing the event takes place. In the case of weather it is the day when weather conditions are recorded as having occurred within a calendar month and 'they are on average more frequent than once in ten years'. The test is the comparison of the *weather measurements* with the *weather data*. The compensation event can then be notified under clause 61.3 and its effect can be assessed at the end of the month when the extent of the weather exceeding the ten-year return *weather data* is known. The process starts again at the beginning of each month.

This compensation event is concerned with weather occurring only at the place stated in the Contract Data. If weather occurring at some distance from the Site could produce some risk such as flooding on the Site, the allocation of risk should be dealt with by special compensation events.

It should be noted that the ECC awards both time and money to the contractor who successfully proves a weather compensation event. Traditional contracts tend to award an extension of time but no money and, for this reason, some employers are unhappy at having to pay for an event that is not within their control in the same way that the other events are within their control. Many employers have deleted this clause using Option Z. Perhaps these employers are not aware of how onerous the weather compensation event actually is, and how much risk the contractor is actually adopting already. This point is worth emphasising since it is a common misconception that the ECC weather statement is less onerous than in traditional contracts.

The criterion is weather that occurs on average less frequently than once in ten years. Let us say that there has been a large amount of rainfall in May. The *Contractor* wishes to notify a compensation event. He should first, having measured the rainfall at the place stated in the Contract Data (hopefully on or near the Site), average the rainfall received in that May. He should then access records that give the rainfall of every May for the past nine years.[24] The average rainfall for each May month is then compared. If the average rainfall in the May month during which the *Contractor* was Providing the Works was higher than all of the nine other May averages, then the compensation event may be notified. If the relevant May month was the same as the highest May average,

---

[22]The Met office web page www.met-office.gov.uk has a section dedicated to NEC Planning Averages and NEC Monthly Updates. You can subscribe to this service by contacting the Met Office email construction@metoffice.gov.uk.
[23]ECC3 Contract Data part one requires the insertion of who is to supply the *weather measurements*.
[24]The records from the Met office tend to give a 'ten-year average', making comparisons much easier.

then it does not fit the criterion since it would then be equal to, not less than once in ten years.

Scenario 1

The average rainfall for the month of May in the relevant year (in this case 2006) and the nine preceding years is as follows:

2006	2005	2004	2003	2002	2001	2000	1999	1998	1997
144	125	114	130	137	141	127	133	140	143

The average rainfall in 2006 is the highest and therefore fits the criterion of occurring on average less frequently than once in ten years. The rainfall may be notified as a compensation event under clause 60.1(13).

Scenario 2

The average rainfall for the month of May in the relevant year (in this case 2006) and the nine preceding years is as follows:

2006	2005	2004	2003	2002	2001	2000	1999	1998	1997
142	125	114	130	137	141	127	133	140	**143**

The average rainfall in 2006 is the second highest and therefore does not fit the criterion of occurring on average less frequently than once in ten years. The rainfall may not be notified as a compensation event under clause 60.1(13).

Scenario 3

The average rainfall for the month of May in the relevant year (in this case 2006) and the nine preceding years is as follows:

2006	2005	2004	2003	2002	2001	2000	1999	1998	1997
143	125	114	130	137	141	127	133	140	143

The average rainfall in 2006 is the highest, but this highest has occurred previously in the last ten years. The rainfall does not fit the criterion of occurring on average less frequently than once in ten years. The rainfall may not be notified as a compensation event under clause 60.1(13).

Through these examples it can be seen that the *Contractor* is required to measure the *weather measurement*s such as rainfall and compare them with the *weather data* that show the information for the last nine years. Only if the *weather measurement* is the highest in ten years does the compensation event fit. Note that the examples illustrate how the ten-year average would work. In practice, records from the Met office show a ten-year average and an easier comparison.

It makes sense that the *Employer* takes the risk for elements that are outwith the *Contractor*'s control. If the *Contractor* is to take the risk, he is likely to factor this risk into the contract and the *Employer* is unlikely to know whether he is receiving value for money. The *Contractor* is likely to be conservative in his risk estimate and the true price of the project could be difficult to assess.

In ECC3 this has been clarified so that it is clear that it applies to the 'extra' weather and not to the ten-year weather which is at the *Contractor*'s risk.

Compensation event 60.1(14)

ECC2: '60.1(14) An *Employer*'s risk event occurs.'

ECC3: '60.1(14) The wording is amended as follows:

"An event which is an *Employer*'s risk stated in this contract".'

The wording has been amended to reflect that this clause does not just refer to clause 80.1, which lists *Employer*'s risks but also includes any additional *Employer*'s risks stated in the Contract Data.

Clause 80.1 of the ECC lists the *Employer*'s risks. Additional *Employer*'s risks, if any exist, are stated in part one of the Contract Data. Those *Employers* providing design to the *Contractor* should note that an *Employer*'s risk event is claims, proceedings, compensation, and claims that are due to a fault of the *Employer* or a fault in his design.

Compensation event 60.1(15)

'60.1(15)   The *Project Manager* certifies take over of a part of the works before both Completion and the Completion Date.'

The *Employer* may use a part of the *works* before Completion and, unless the use is for reasons stated in Clause 35.3,[25] he takes over that part. If take over occurs before Completion **and** the Completion Date, it is a compensation event.

It is important to note that the Works Information should state the reasons, if any exist, as to why the *Employer* may require to use part of the *works* before Completion. For example, the *Employer* could require access across parts of the *works* for his own requirements. Alternatively, the *Contractor* may request the *Employer* to use part of the *works* to suit his method of working. Under clause 35.3[26] of the ECC, take over would **not** occur in either of these instances and therefore there would be no compensation event. The *Employer* may state in Contract Data part one that he is unwilling to take over the *works* before the Completion Date (to cover instances where the *Contractor* completes early and expects the *employer* to take over early).

Compensation event 60.1(16)

'60.1(16)   The *Employer* does not provide materials, facilities and samples for tests [ECC3 the words ''and inspections'' inserted here] as stated in the Works Information.'

Clause 40.2 of the ECC requires the *Employer* to provide materials, facilities and samples for tests and inspections as stated in the Works Information. This compensation event relies on the Works Information stating the things that the *Employer* is to provide. If the *Employer* does not provide the things he is required to provide, then the *Contractor* is entitled to notify a compensation event.

Compensation event 60.1(17)

ECC2: '60.1(17)   The *Project Manager* notifies a correction to an assumption about the nature of a compensation event.'

ECC3: '60.1(17)   The wording is amended as follows:

''The *Project Manager* notifies a correction to an assumption which he has stated about the nature of a compensation event.''

The wording has been amended to reflect that the compensation event only relates to assumptions made by the *Project Manager* and not those made by the *Contractor*.

Clause 61.6 allows the *Project Manager* to state assumptions to be used to facilitate the assessment of a compensation event. If he later notifies the *Contractor* of corrections to these assumptions, the notification is a separate compensation event.

Compensation event 60.1(18)

'60.1(18)   A breach of contract by the *Employer* which is not one of the other compensation events in this contract.'

This is an 'umbrella' clause to include breaches of contract by the *Employer* within the compensation event procedure.

[25]ECC3 clause 35.2.
[26]ECC3 clause 35.2.

Compensation event 60.1(19) (ECC3 only)
ECC3: '60.1(19)

"An event which

- stops the *Contractor* completing the *works* or
- stops the *Contractor* completing the *works* by the date shown on the accepted programme, and which
- neither Party could prevent,
- an experienced contractor would have judged at the Contract Date to have such a small chance of occurring that it would have been unreasonable for him to have allowed for it,
- is not one of the other compensation events stated in this contract".'

This compensation event deals with events where the chances of it happening are so remote as it to be unreasonable to have included for it in the contract.

No attempt has been made as with other contracts to define what it is (e.g. war, act of God). A legal definition of force majeure is as follows:

'**Force Majeure** [French] Irresistible compulsion or coercion. The phrase is used particularly in commercial contracts to describe events possibly affecting the contract and that are completely outside the parties' control. Such events are normally listed in full to ensure their enforceability; they may include acts of God, fires, failure of suppliers or subcontractors to supply the supplier under the agreement, and strikes and other labour disputes that interfere with the supplier's performance of an agreement. An express clause would normally excuse both delay and a total failure to perform the agreement.'

(Oxford dictionary of law fourth edition 1997, Oxford University Press.)

This new clause will also make it a positive obligation on the *Contractor* to notify such events.

An example of a situation where this compensation event could be used is a foot-and-mouth epedemic. The epidemic which occurred in 2001 in the UK had a severe effect on pipe laying and other projects in areas affected by the disease.

Summary of clauses referred to in the compensation events
Table 1.1 gives an at-a-glance summary of the compensation event clauses.

1.4.2 Main Options B and D only
Since Options B and D are fully reimbursable, there are three additional compensation events applicable to these main Options only under the contract as follows.

Compensation event 60.4
'ECC2: 60.4   A difference between the final total quantity of work done and the quantity stated for an item in the *bill of quantities* at the Contract Date is a compensation event if

- the difference causes the Actual Cost per unit of quantity to change and
- the rate in the *bill of quantities* for the item at the Contract Date multiplied by the final total quantity of work done is more than 0.1% of the total of the Prices at the Contract Date.

If the Actual Cost per unit of quantity is reduced, the affected rate is reduced.'

A change in quantity is not, in itself, a compensation event. A compensation event is triggered only by the changed quantity satisfying the two tests stated in the clause.

This clause only applies to changes in quantities, which do not result from changes to the Works Information. A change to the Works Information is always a compensation event, subject to the exceptions in clause 60.1(1), regardless of the effect on quantities.

Table 1.1. Summary of compensation event clauses

Clause	Brief description	Relevant clause in the ECC (brackets ECC3)
60.1(1)	Change to the Works Information	Clause 14.3 and 29.1 (ECC3 27.3) and 44
60.1(2)	Possession of the Site	Clause 33.1
60.1(3)	*Employer* providing something	Clause 31.2
60.1(4)	Stop or not start any work	Clause 34.1
60.1(5)	*Employer* and others working times and conditions	Clause 31.2
60.1(6)	Replying to communications	Clause 13.3
60.1(7)	Object of value	Clause 73.1
60.1(8)	Changing decisions	No specific clause
60.1(9)	Withholding acceptance	Clause 13.8 and for example 13.4, 24.1, 31.3
60.1(10)	Instructions to search	Clause 42.1
60.1(11)	Test or inspection causing delay	Clause 40.5
60.1(12)	Physical conditions	See also clauses 60.2 and 60.3
60.1(13)	Weather	No specific clause
60.1(14)	*Employer*'s risk	Clause 80.1
60.1(15)	Take over	Clause 35.3 (ECC3 clause 35.2)
60.1(16)	*Employer* provides materials, facilities and samples	Clause 40.2
60.1(17)	Correction to an assumption	Clause 61.6
60.1(18)	Breach of contract	No specific clause
60.1(19)	Unforeseen event	(New clause in ECC3)

ECC3: '60.4   The wording is amended as follows:

"A difference between the final total quantity of work done and the quantity stated for an item in the Bill of Quantities is a compensation event if:

- The difference does not result from a change to the Works Information,
- the difference causes the Defined Cost per unit of quantity to change and
- the rate in the Bill of Quantities for the item multiplied by the final total quantity of work done is more than 0.5% of the total of the Prices at the Contract Date.

If the Defined Cost per unit of quantity is reduced, the affected rate is reduced".'

The amendments address the following points. The introduction of the first bullet point makes the point clear that it does not refer to changes in the Works Information which are always compensation events and the percentage change has been increased from 0.1% to 0.5%. This increases the threshold at which a change in quantity becomes a compensation event.

This means the *Contractor* carries the risk of changes up to 0.5%.

Compensation event 60.5
'ECC2: 60.5   A difference between the final total quantity of work done and the quantity for an item stated in the *bill of quantities* at the Contract Date which delays Completion is a compensation event.'

A difference between original and final quantities in a *bill of quantities* is not, in itself, a compensation event. The amount due to the *Contractor* includes the

Price for Work Done to Date, which is based on the actual quantities of work done. However, any difference of quantities, which causes Completion to be delayed, is a compensation event.

ECC3: '60.5   The wording is amended as follows:

"A difference between the final total quantity of work done and the quantity for an item stated in the Bill of Quantities which delays Completion is a compensation event or the meeting of the Condition stated for a Key Date, is a compensation event''.'

A difference between original and final quantities in a Bill of Quantities is not, in itself, a compensation event. The amount due to the *Contractor* includes the Price for Work Done to Date, which is based on the actual quantities of work done. However, any difference of quantities, which causes Completion to be delayed or delays a Key Date, is a compensation event.

Compensation event 60.6

ECC2: '60.6   The *Project Manager* corrects mistakes in the *bill of quantities* which are departures from the *method of measurement* or are due to ambiguities or inconsistencies. Each such correction is a compensation event which may lead to reduced Prices.'

Since the *bill of quantities* is not Works Information,[27] any mistakes in the *bill of quantities* arising because the bill does not comply with the *method of measurement* or because of ambiguities or inconsistencies are treated separately.[28] This may occur when an item has been omitted from the bill or an item in the bill should be deleted or amended to comply with the *method of measurement*. This is one of the compensation events, which may result in a reduction of the Prices.

ECC3: '60.6   The wording is amended as follows:

"The *Project Manager* corrects mistakes in the Bills of Quantities which are departures from the *method of measurement* or are due to ambiguities or inconsistencies. Each such correction is a compensation event which may lead to reduced Prices''.'

1.4.3 Secondary Options J,[29] T,[30] U[31] and Y(UK)2 and X15 in ECC3

Should any one of these secondary options form part of a contract, it should be noted that by including them, there are additional compensation events.

Option J: Advanced payment to the *Contractor*[32]

If there is a delay in the *Employer*'s making the advanced payment under this secondary Option, a compensation event occurs.

Option T: Changes in the law[33]

If, after the Contract Date, a change in the *law of this contract* occurs, it is a compensation event.

Option U: The Construction (Design and Management) Regulations 1994 (to be used for contracts in the UK)[34]

A delay to the work or additional or changed work caused by the application of these regulations is a compensation event, if an experienced contractor could not reasonably be expected to have foreseen it.

---

[27]Clause 55.1.
[28]See clause 17.
[29]ECC secondary Option X14.
[30]ECC3 secondary Option X2.
[31]ECC3 no secondary Option U (CDM Regulations): presumed considered covered by clause 27.4 – CDM is UK specific and ECC is an international contract.
[32]ECC3 secondary Option X14.
[33]ECC3 secondary Option X2.
[34]ECC3 no secondary Option U (CDM Regulations): presumed considered covered by clause 27.4 – CDM is UK specific and ECC is an international contract.

Option Y(UK)2: Part II of the Housing Grants, Construction and Regeneration Act 1996[35]
Suspension of performance is a compensation event if the *Contractor* exercises his right to suspend performance under the Act.

Option X15 (ECC3): Limitation of the *Contractor*'s liability for his design to reasonable skill and care if the *Contractor* corrects a Defect for which he is not liable under the contract, it is a compensation event.

1.4.4 Contract Data (part one) The *Employer* is able to include any additional compensation events he requires in Contract Data part one. These events will be specific for each individual contract. They must be defined unambiguously in order to avoid any future disputes because by including them, the risk of costs and delay arising from the event passes to the *Employer*.

The *Employer* is also able to insert additional *Employer*'s risk in Contract Data part one. The *Employer* may wish for example to include those risks that, if the *Contractor* bore them, would be uneconomical. These also then become compensation events under clause 60.1(14).

> In ECC2 additional compensation events can be found in Options B, D, J, T, U, Y(UK)2 and Contract Data part one.
>
> In ECC3 additional compensation events can be found in Options B, D, Option X14 (ECC2 Option J), Option X2 (ECC2 Option T), U, Y(UK)2, X15 and Contract Data part one.

1.5 Roles of the *Project Manager* and *Contractor*

The roles of the *Project Manager* and *Contractor* in the compensation event procedure are defined in the ECC in terms of the actions each is to take. These actions are all described in section 6 of the core clauses – 'Compensation Events'.[36]

The list of compensation events contained within clause 60.1 divide generally into two categories:

(1) those for which the *Project Manager* will usually volunteer a decision that a compensation event has occurred; that is, those generally in respect of instructions issued by the *Project Manager* or *Supervisor*[37] and

(2) those which, due to their subjectivity or because the event could be construed as some shortcoming of the *Project Manager*, *Supervisor* or *Employer*, it is more likely to be left to the *Contractor* to notify the *Project Manager* that he considers a compensation event has occurred.[38]

Appendix 1, Sections D and E show the different procedures to be followed in each case. It will be seen that the procedures are identical once the *Project Manager*, for events in the second of the above categories, notifies the *Contractor* that he believes a compensation event has occurred.

The flow charts in Appendix 1 show the 'trouble-free' situations where the procedure operates smoothly. In practice, however, complicating factors can arise to disrupt the smooth process envisaged, but which in fairness to the ECC have been predicted and provided for in the Contract. Appendix 1F shows a table of the more common complicating factors that can arise and some possible consequences.

[35]ECC3 clause Y2.3 of secondary Option Y(UK)2.
[36]Appendix 1, Sections A and B list those actions required by the *Project Manager* and *Contractor* with regard to compensation events.
[37]See section 1.7.2 below.
[38]See section 1.7.3 below.

1.6 Administering compensation events

The assessment of a compensation event is always of its effect on both cost (the Prices) and programme (the Completion Date and Key Dates[39]).

1.6.1 Changes to the Completion Date

The *Contractor* includes a revised programme[40] as part of his quotation for the compensation event where the programme has altered in any way. A change to the programme includes not only a change to the Completion Date or Key Dates,[41] but changes to the resources, method statement[42] or sequencing of the programme. In any of these cases, a revised programme[43] is required to be submitted with the quotation.

> Compensation events are a package of time and money; therefore, the programme is a part of a quotation for a compensation event.

The programme is an important part of a compensation event quotation. The *Contractor* should ensure that all changes are noted on the programme, including consequential changes that result from a compensation event.

1.6.2 Changes to the Prices

Clause 63.1 of the ECC states that the changes to the Prices are assessed as the effect of the compensation event upon the Actual Cost[44] of the work already done, the forecast Actual Cost[45] of the work not yet done and the resulting Fee.

The important principle here is that there is absolutely no reference to the Prices included in the *activity schedules*[46] (main Options A except where agreed[47] and C) or the *bill of quantities*[48] (main Option B and D except where agreed[49]); that is, the tendered rates. The Prices in main Options C and D are used to determine the target price only. Instead, assessment of the financial effects of a compensation event is based on their effect on Actual Cost[50] plus the Fee.

Actual Cost[51] is defined in all main Options. The Fee is the amount calculated by applying the tendered *fee percentage* (*direct fee percentage* and *subcontracted fee percentage* in ECC3) stated in Contract Data part two to the amount of Actual/Defined Cost and is intended to cover such items as the *Contractor*'s off-site overheads, profit and any other cost components not expressly included in the Schedule of Cost Components.[52]

What this all means is that for every compensation event a 'mini-lump sum' price is estimated in advance and is based on its forecast effect on:

- Actual/Defined Cost or
- the Actual/Defined Cost of the work already done, if the assessment is made after the work because the subject of the compensation event has been completed.

No compensation event for which a quotation is required is due to the fault of the *Contractor* or relates to a matter which is at his risk under the contract. It is

---

[39]ECC3 only.
[40]Called in ECC3 'alterations to the Accepted Programme'.
[41]ECC3 only.
[42]Referred to in ECC3 as a statement of how the *Contractor* plans to do the work.
[43]ECC3: alterations to the Accepted Programme.
[44]ECC3 Defined Cost.
[45]ECC3 Defined Cost.
[46]ECC3 clause A and C11.2(20) Activity Schedule is a defined term.
[47]ECC3 clause A63.14.
[48]ECC3 clause B and D11.2(21) Bills of Quantities is a defined term.
[49]ECC2 clause 63.9; ECC3 clause 63.13.
[50]ECC3 Defined Cost.
[51]ECC3 Defined Cost.
[52]See clause 52.1.

therefore appropriate to reimburse the *Contractor* his forecast additional costs (or actual additional costs if the work has already been done).

1.6.3 Procedure for change

1.6.3.1 Forecasts

It is the intention of the ECC that the majority of quotations for compensation events are based on forecasts of their financial effects (provided by the time-scales included in the contract) since this accords with the objective designed to provide the *Employer* with reasonable certainty of the cost and time implications of changes to the work and places a risk on the *Contractor*, which motivates him to manage the new situation efficiently.

Where the effects of a change are too uncertain to be forecast reasonably by the *Contractor*, the *Project Manager* states assumptions about the event on which the *Contractor* bases his forecast of Actual Cost.[53] This precludes the use of large contingent sums in the *Contractor*'s quotations. The *Project Manager*'s assumptions provide the only mechanism for revisiting the compensation event quotation after implementation.

1.6.3.2 Revisiting compensation events

The quotation provided by the *Contractor* is his **only** chance of including **all** costs (consequential or otherwise) resulting from a particular event. Once a compensation event has been implemented, only the *Project Manager*'s assumptions that turn out to be incorrect allow the revisiting of a quotation.[54] Any assumptions made by the *Contractor*, if later proved to be incorrect, do not allow such reassessment. This must be made abundantly clear to *Contractors*.

1.6.3.3 Times stated in the procedure

In practice many compensation events can occur simultaneously and some compensation events may involve significant restructuring of the price document (and programme). In recognition of this the ECC allows the relaxation of the time periods by agreement between the *Project Manager* and the *Contractor*.[55] Such relaxation, however, should be the exception to the rule and not used as a cover-up for ineffective or poor contract administration.

It may be the case that the *Project Manager* has been given a specific level of financial authorisation and that he would be required to report to a management board on increases to the project value. He could therefore find it difficult to respond in the time required by the contract where a compensation event has breached the maximum level of his financial authority, whether per event or total contract value. This would apply particularly to the two-week reply to quotations.

Where the *Employer* wishes to initiate specific procedures covering this scenario, amendments to the *conditions of contract* can be made using Option Z. For one-off cases, the *Project Manager* should rely on clause 62.5 to extend the time required.

Variations in the *Contractor*'s supply chain could also result in the *Contractor* needing an extension to the time period of three weeks to submit a quotation for a compensation event.

In general, agreement on time-scales should probably be made for each compensation event as it arises, so that the right resolution is arrived at practically while still reflecting the spirit of the contract.

1.6.3.4 Other aspects of the procedure

The compensation event process has specific procedural requirements, which fall into three distinct stages, namely:

(1)   notification,
(2)   quotation,
(3)   implementation.

[53]Clause 61.6 ECC3 Actual Cost is termed Defined Cost.
[54]See clauses 61.6 and 60.1(17).
[55]See clauses 61.4 and 62.5.

> Quotations cannot be revisited unless they are based on assumptions given by the *Project Manager* and he later corrects incorrect assumptions.

1.6.4 Cost of preparing for quotations

Under Options A and B, the *Contractor* may not claim for the cost of preparing quotations for compensation events.[56] This is probably because few compensation events should take place under Options A and B contracts due to their being priced contracts. Any compensation events that take place should be relatively small.

The *Contractor* should be aware of this and cater for any costs in his *fee percentage* (*direct fee percentage* or *subcontracted fee percentage* in ECC3). If a large compensation event takes place, the *Contractor* may choose to request the reimbursement of its preparation costs as part of the compensation event. The *Project Manager* needs to make a decision outwith the contract in this instance.

Quotations for compensation events may include the cost of their preparation under main Options other than Options A and B.

> The cost of preparing quotations is included in the *fee percentage* for Options A and B contracts.

1.7 Notification of a compensation event

1.7.1 Proposed instruction or changed decision

Note that although this sub-heading is included under the heading of compensation event, the instruction of such a quotation is **not** a compensation event in itself.

The *Project Manager* may instruct the *Contractor* to submit quotations for a proposed instruction or a proposed changed decision.[57] The quotation is to be submitted within three weeks of being instructed to do so by the *Project Manager*,[58] but this may be extended by agreement.[59]

The instruction is **not** related to a compensation event *per se* but only to a potential compensation event, and the *Project Manager* should make this very clear in his instruction. This option is available to the *Project Manager* where he may be considering a change but wishes first to know what the effect of that change would be. Once he has received the no-obligation quotation, he has the option of not issuing the instruction[60] (or changed decision) where perhaps the quotation would affect the budget or the programme too much. If the quotation is suitable to him, he may then notify a compensation event in accordance with clause 61.1.

Since the quotation has already been submitted, the resulting compensation event procedure could be somewhat reduced because the compensation event could be implemented directly after the compensation event notification.[61]

> The *Project Manager* may request a quotation for something he is thinking of changing.

---

[56]ECC2 clause 11.2(28); ECC3 clause 11.2(22) preparing quotations becomes Disallowed Cost.
[57]Clause 61.2.
[58]Clause 62.3.
[59]Clause 62.5.
[60]Clause 62.3.
[61]Clause 65.1.

1.7.2 Notification by the Project Manager

Either the *Contractor* or the *Project Manager* can notify a compensation event. There are seven instances in which the *Project Manager* should identify the compensation event.[62]

(1) The *Project Manager* gives an instruction changing the Works Information.[63]

(2) The *Project Manager* gives an instruction to stop or not to start any work.[64]

(3) The *Project Manager* gives an instruction for dealing with an object of value or of historical or other interest found within the Site.[65]

(4) The *Project Manager* or the *Supervisor*[66] changes a decision which he has previously communicated to the *Contractor*.[67]

(5) The *Supervisor* instructs the *Contractor* to search and no Defect is found (unless the search is needed only because the *Contractor* gave insufficient notice of doing work obstructing a required test or inspection).[68]

(6) The *Project Manager* certifies take over of a part of the *works* before both Completion and the Completion Date (unless this is for a reason stated in the Works Information or to suit the *Contractor*'s way of working).[69]

(7) The *Project Manager* notifies a correction to an assumption about the nature of a compensation event.[70]

If the *Project Manager* does not notify a compensation event, the *Contractor* may do so.[71] Although the *Project Manager* may therefore rely on the *Contractor* to notify all compensation events, even those that he, the *Project Manager*, should notify, it falls within the boundaries of mutual trust and cooperation that the *Project Manager* notifies those compensation events that he is required to notify.

> If the *Project Manager* does not notify a compensation event, the *Contractor* may do so.

1.7.3 Notification by the Contractor

The *Contractor* may notify a compensation event under the following circumstances:[72]

- the *Contractor* believes the event is a compensation event,
- it is less than two weeks since he became aware of the event[73] and
- the *Project Manager* has not notified the event to the *Contractor*.

Note that all three statements have to be satisfied before the *Contractor* may notify a compensation event to the *Project Manager*. In ECC3, the eight weeks within which the *Contractor* should notify a compensation event may become an indefinite period if it is a compensation event which the *Project Manager* should have notified but did not.[74] This is an encouragement to the *Project Manager* to notify compensation events. It could also potentially result in the traditional

---

[62]Clause 61.1.
[63]Clause 60.1(1).
[64]Clause 60.1(4); ECC3 includes Key Date.
[65]Clause 60.1(7).
[66]The assumption is made that the *Project Manager* is aware of the *Supervisor*'s changing a decision, presumably because he has been copied in on correspondence or because the *Supervisor* has informed him of the change.
[67]Clause 60.1(8).
[68]Clause 60.1(10).
[69]Clause 60.1(15).
[70]Clause 60.1(17).
[71]Clause 61.3. In ECC3 if the *Contractor* does not notify of a compensation event within eight weeks of becoming aware of the event, he is not entitled to the compensation event unless the *Project Manager* should have notified the event to the *Contractor* but did not.
[72]Clause 61.3.
[73]ECC3 now eight weeks in lieu of two weeks.
[74]ECC3 clause 61.3.

'claims' situation, where compensation events are notified so long after the actual event that it is difficult to assess its impact.

1.7.3.1 Believing the event is a compensation event

The *Contractor* would usually believe that an event is a compensation event if he or his *works* have been affected in some way. At this stage the *Contractor* does not need to confine himself to the compensation events in the contract, although clearly not doing so may lead to the notification failing the four-point test in clause 61.4.

1.7.3.2 Less than two weeks since he became aware of the event[75]

This is an objective test that may be evidenced by documentation. The ECC sets this time limit to force issues to the fore and ensure that they are dealt with promptly, thereby maintaining the certainty of the final outcome, vital to upholding a good working relationship between the parties throughout the contract.

> The *Contractor* has only two weeks (ECC3 eight weeks) to notify a compensation event from becoming aware of it.

In ECC3: '61.3   If the *Contractor* does not notify a compensation event within eight weeks of becoming aware of the event he is not entitled to a change in Prices, the Completion Date or Key Date unless the *Project Manager* should have notified the event to the *Contractor* but did not.'

'61.4   A failure by the *Project Manager* to reply within two weeks of this notification is treated as acceptance by the *Project Manager* that the event is a compensation event and an instruction to submit a quotation.'

1.7.3.3 The Project Manager *has not notified the event*

If the *Project Manager* has notified the events that he should have notified in accordance with clause 61.1, then the events that are left to the *Contractor* to identify are:[76]

(1)   A failure by the *Employer*, *Project Manager*, *Supervisor* or Others to fulfil their obligations (compensation events 2, 3, 5, 6, 11, 16 and 18).
(2)   The *Project Manager* withholding an acceptance for a reason not stated in the contract (compensation event 9).
(3)   An *Employer*'s risk event occurs (compensation event 14).
(4)   A happening not caused by any party (compensation events 12, 13 and 19).
(5)   Events confined to the main and secondary Options and any additional compensation events stated in the Contract Data.

In reality, however, the *Contractor* would be advised to notify all events that he considers to be compensation events, even those that the *Project Manager* is supposed to notify but does not.

The occurrence of a compensation event entitles the *Contractor* to an **assessment** of time and money.[77] The *Contractor*'s notifying an event does not necessarily mean that he will receive time and money for the event because there is still the four-point test carried out by the *Project Manager* on receiving a notification from the *Contractor*.

1.7.4 The four-point test

Once the *Contractor* has notified a compensation event, the *Project Manager* assesses the event against a four-point test as follows:[78]

---

[75]ECC3 now eight weeks in lieu of two weeks.
[76]Partly taken from the ECC2 guidance notes page 61.
[77]As opposed to immediately entitling him to time and money; the assessment might be zero.
[78]Clause 61.4.

Question	Yes	No
1. Does the event arise from a fault of the *Contractor*?		✓
2. Has the event happened or is it expected to happen?	✓	
3. Does the event affect Actual Cost[79] or Completion?[80]	✓	
4. Is the event one of the compensation events stated in this contract?	✓	

Note that all four parts of the test have to be passed. Note also that if the ticks were to be placed in any other blocks, the test would fail.

Whether the event will ever happen may be a matter of opinion, as is whether the Prices, Completion (or Key Dates in ECC3) would be affected. The first and the last points are reasonably objective, however.

If the notification passes the test, then the *Project Manager* instructs the *Contractor* to submit quotations for the event. If the notification fails the test, then the *Project Manager* informs the *Contractor* that the Prices, the Completion Date (and the Key Dates in ECC3) will not be changed and the compensation event procedure ends. Of course, if the *Contractor* is unhappy with the *Project Manager*'s decision, he may take the matter to adjudication.

Compensation events notified by the *Project Manager* do not go through this test. This is presumably because the *Project Manager* has already decided that the event was not the *Contractor*'s fault and the event has already happened, and it is one of the compensation events stated in the contract. Whether the Prices and the Completion Date (and the Key Dates in ECC3) will be affected will be determined after the quotation has been received.

1.8 Quotations for compensation event

1.8.1 Introduction A quotation is a time and money 'package' of the *Contractor*'s assessment (unless it is a *Project Manager*'s assessment) of the financial and time effects of the compensation event, and should be submitted within three weeks (or such other agreed period) of the *Project Manager*'s instruction to do so.

1.8.2 When are quotations submitted? There are three instances in which a *Contractor* may be instructed by the *Project Manager* to submit quotations in relation to compensation events:[81]

(1) The *Project Manager* instructs the *Contractor* to submit quotations for a compensation event at the same time as he notifies the compensation event.[82]

(2) The *Project Manager* instructs the *Contractor* to submit quotations for a compensation event once he has decided that an event notified by the *Contractor* has passed the four-point test.[83] Note that this is in the alternative to number 1 above; the two cannot happen for the same event.

(3) The *Project Manager* instructs the *Contractor* to submit a **revised** quotation for a compensation event.[84]

In all three instances, the *Contractor* has three weeks within which to submit quotations,[85] but this time may be extended by agreement between the *Contractor* and the *Project Manager* before the quotation is due.[86] If the

---

[79]ECC3 Defined Cost.
[80]ECC3 adds 'or meeting a Key Date'.
[81]The *Contractor* may also be required to submit quotations for acceleration (clause 36.1) or for the acceptance of a Defect (clause 44.2), in which case the quotations are submitted within the *period for reply*.
[82]Clause 61.1.
[83]Clause 61.4.
[84]Clause 62.3.
[85]Clause 62.3 for instances 1 and 2; clause 62.4 for instance 3.
[86]Clause 62.5; see additional requirements in ECC3 clause 62.6.

Contractor does not submit his quotation and its accompanying details within the required time, the *Project Manager* will assess the compensation event himself, a powerful disincentive for the *Contractor*.

In addition to quotations as a result of a compensation event notification, the *Project Manager* may also instruct the *Contractor* to submit quotations for a proposed instruction (or changed decision), as discussed in section 1.7.1 above, which could also result in a compensation event.

1.8.3 Instructions for quotations

An instruction to submit a quotation could include the following:

- A notification that the *Contractor* did not give an early warning of an event that an experienced contractor could have given.[87]
- Assumptions about the event where the *Project Manager* decides that the effects of a compensation event are too uncertain to be forecast reasonably.[88]
- An instruction to submit alternative quotations based on different ways of dealing with the compensation event.[89] This is particularly useful where the *Project Manager* wishes to retain the Completion Date.[90]

1.8.4 What is included in the quotation?

Quotations for compensation events comprise:[91]

- proposed changes to the Prices and
- any delay to the Completion Date and
- in ECC3, any delay to the Key Dates

assessed by the *Contractor*.

The quotations also include the following:

- Details of the assessment of the changes to the Prices and the delay to the Completion Date.[92]
- A revised programme[93] showing the effect of the compensation event where the programme for the remaining work has been affected.[94]
- Cost and time risk allowances for matters which have a significant chance of occurring and are at the *Contractor*'s risk under the contract.[95]
- Alternative quotations where instructed to do so by the *Project Manager*.[96]
- Alternative quotations for other methods of dealing with the compensation event which the *Contractor* considers practicable.[97]

> The *Contractor* may include alternative quotations.

If the *Project Manager* has notified the *Contractor* in his instruction to submit quotations that the *Contractor* did not give an early warning that an experienced contractor could have given, then the *Contractor* assesses the quotation as if he had given an early warning.[98] This is the sanction on the *Contractor* for

---

[87]Clause 61.5.

[88]Clause 61.6.

[89]Clause 62.1. In ECC3, the *Project Manager* must first discuss the different ways of dealing with the compensation event which are practicable.

[90]Where a compensation event is likely to result in a delay to the Completion Date but the *Project Manager* is keen to retain the Completion Date, rather than accelerating, the *Project Manager* could request alternative quotations for the compensation event, retaining the Completion Date in one of the alternatives.

[91]Clause 62.2.

[92]Clause 62.2. ECC3 includes Key Dates.

[93]Clause 62.2. ECC3 refers to 'alterations to the Accepted Programme' rather than a revised programme.

[94]Note that the programme is required if the remaining work is affected, not only if the Completion Date has changed. In other words, if a method or resource statement has changed, sequencing amended or durations affected, a revised programme is required.

[95]ECC2 clause 63.5; ECC3 clause 63.6.

[96]Clause 61.6.

[97]Clause 62.1.

[98]ECC2 clause 63.4; ECC3 clause 63.5.

---

not following the early warning procedure in the contract. The event is therefore assessed as if the options that would have been available at the time that an early warning could have been given are still available and the quotation is for the most effective and economical option.

The quotation is based on the assumption that:

- the *Contractor* reacts competently and promptly to the compensation event,
- the additional Actual/Defined Cost and time due to the event are reasonably incurred and
- the Accepted Programme can be changed.[99]

1.8.4.1 Changes to the Prices

Changes to the Prices are assessed as the effect of the compensation event upon:[100]

- the Actual Cost[101] of the work already done,
- the forecast Actual Cost[102] of the work not yet done and
- the resulting Fee.

Actual Cost[103]

The first thing to notice is that all payment mechanisms[104] deal with compensation events in the same way. That is, all compensation events are assessed using Actual Cost[105] as defined, which, for all main Options except Option F, include the Schedule of Cost Components. This means that for Options A and B, which use an *activity schedule* and a *bill of quantities*[106] as the payment mechanism rather than Actual Cost,[107] changes and other compensation events are not assessed using the *activity schedule* or the *bill of quantities*.[108] Compensation events under Options A and B are assessed using the Schedule of Cost Components.

The effect of the event

Second, the assessment is the **effect** of the compensation event upon the three items of cost. The event is therefore the basis for all assessment and its effect needs to be determined.

Works already done

The calculation includes the effect upon work already done and the effect upon work not yet done. The work already done may refer to work that has been completed and that is now required to be changed. It is not the bill cost (Option B) or the activity cost (Option A) that is assessed, but the Actual/Defined Cost of the work. The chances of a *Contractor* having maintained records from which this information can be extracted are possibly small, and compiling this information could be taxing. The calculation is that the Actual/Defined Cost of the work done is deducted and the forecast Actual/Defined Cost of the new work is added.

Forecast of work not yet done

The calculation of work not yet done is a forecast. The assumption is that the work has not yet been done, although, since the *Contractor* is required to carry out the work and given the time periods of the compensation event procedure, it is possible that the work to be done may already have been done by the time for the submission of the quotation. This would certainly make it easier for the *Contractor* when preparing his quotation. It would reduce some of his risk, and

---

[99]ECC2 clause 63.6; ECC3 clause 63.7.
[100]Clause 63.1.
[101]ECC3 Defined Cost.
[102]ECC3 Defined Cost.
[103]ECC3 Defined Cost.
[104]Except Option F where it is assumed that Subcontractors do most of the work.
[105]ECC3 Defined Cost.
[106]ECC3 Activity Schedule and Bill of Quantities.
[107]ECC3 Defined Cost.
[108]Unless agreed between the *Contractor* and the *Project Manager* in accordance with clauses ECC2 B63.9, ECC3 A63.14, ECC3 B63.13.

in Options C and D would keep the target cost more stable in comparison with the Price for Work Done to Date.

Where this is not the case, the *Contractor* is required to forecast the cost using the Schedule of Cost Components and any Subcontractor quotations. Assumptions about the event made by the *Project Manager* could assist in this forecast.

The Fee

The Fee is defined as the amount calculated by applying the *fee percentage*[109] to the amount of Actual Cost*.[110] The *fee percentage* (*direct* and *subcontracted fee percentage* in ECC3) is tendered by the *Contractor* and is included in his Contract Data part two. It represents his profit and the overheads that are not included elsewhere in the Schedule of Cost Components. Once the *Contractor* has added all the components of cost in the Schedule of Cost Components, added Subcontractor costs and deducted Disallowed Cost to get his total Actual/Defined Cost, he multiplies this Actual/Defined Cost by the *fee percentage* (*direct* and *subcontracted fee percentage* in ECC3) and adds this product to the Actual/Defined Cost.

> The Fee includes all the costs not included in the Schedule of Cost Components.

1.8.4.2 Delay to the Completion Date

A delay to the Completion Date is assessed as the length of time that, due to the compensation event, planned Completion is later than planned Completion as shown on the Accepted Programme.[111] In other words, the *Contractor* includes in his programme the date when he plans to complete, as well as the date he is required to complete in accordance with the contract. This planned Completion date must be earlier than the contractual Completion Date. The duration between planned Completion and the Completion Date is the terminal float and this remains the *Contractor*'s to use if, for example, inefficiencies occur that delay planned Completion up to the Completion Date.

For the purposes of compensation events, therefore, the assessment of the time element of the event is based upon **planned Completion** rather than the Completion Date. See Fig. 1.1.

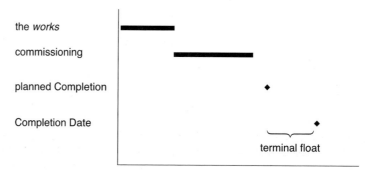

Fig. 1.1. Terminal float

1.8.4.3 Delay to the Key Dates

In ECC3, clauses 63.3 also refers to the delay to a Key Date: a delay to a Key Date is assessed as the length of time that, due to the compensation event, the planned date when the Condition for a Key Date will be met is later than the date shown on the Accepted Programme. In ECC3, the *Contractor* is required to include Key Dates in his programme; that is, the dates by when the *condition*

---

[109] *Direct fee percentage* and *subcontracted fee percentage* in ECC3.
  *Footnote ECC3 Defined Cost.
[110] ECC2 clause 11.2(17); ECC3 clause 11.2(8).
[111] Clause 63.3.

stated in Contract Data part one will be met. A compensation event quotation should include any delay to the Key Date as a result of the compensation event.

1.8.5 Acceptance of a quotation The *Project Manager* is required to respond within two weeks of the *Contractor*'s submitting his quotation,[112] but this time may be extended by agreement between the *Contractor* and the *Project Manager* before the reply is due.[113] His reply may be one of four options:[114]

(1)   an instruction to submit a revised quotation,
(2)   an acceptance of the quotation,
(3)   a notification that a proposed instruction or a proposed changed decision will not be given or
(4)   a notification that he will be making his own assessment.

These four options are further explained as follows:

(1)   The *Project Manager* could give the *Contractor* an instruction to submit a revised quotation after explaining his reasons for doing so.[115] The *Contractor* has three weeks to submit the revised quotation.[116] The *Project Manager* may use this option where, for example, he considers that the assessment has been incorrectly assessed.
(2)   The *Project Manager* could accept the quotation. In this case, the compensation event is implemented.[117]
(3)   The *Project Manager* could give the *Contractor* a notification that a proposed instruction or a proposed changed decision will not be given. This option could be chosen where the *Project Manager* has previously instructed the *Contractor* to submit quotations for a proposed instruction or proposed changed decision,[118] but the resulting quotation shows that the cost of the change is too high or the delay too great[119] and the *Project Manager* does not now wish to make the proposed change.
(4)   The *Project Manager* could give the *Contractor* a notification that he will be making his own assessment. He could do this if, for example, he had already instructed a revised quotation but it was also unsatisfactory, or if he did not believe that a revised quotation would yield the results expected.

1.9 Assessment of quotations

The assessment of the compensation event is assumed to take place by the *Contractor*. The *Contractor* is required to assess the event as if he had given an early warning (where so notified), and to include time and cost risk allowances.

It is only if the *Project Manager* replies to a submitted quotation that he will be making his own assessment, that the *Project Manager* may assess a compensation event. The *Contractor* therefore always gets first chance at assessing the event.

1.9.1 Assessment by the Project Manager It is not really in either Party's interest for the *Project Manager* to assess a compensation event. The *Project Manager* will use the tools available to him, such as the Accepted Programme, which means that the *Contractor* is incentivised to keep his programme accurate and up to date. Since the reasons for the *Project Manager* making his own assessment all originate in some failure of the *Contractor*, it is possible that the *Project Manager* may be a bit more stringent in his calculations than the *Contractor*. It is unlikely that the

[112]Clause 62.3.
[113]Clause 62.5.
[114]Clause 62.3.
[115]Clause 62.4.
[116]Clause 62.4.
[117]Clause 65.1.
[118]Under clause 61.2.
[119]See section 1.7.1 above for a discussion regarding instructions for quotations for a proposed instruction or a proposed changed decision.

Contractor will be happy about this arrangement, but his recourse is through adjudication. It therefore seems sensible that the *Contractor* prevents the compensation event procedure going as far as the *Project Manager* having to do his own assessment.

1.9.1.1 Reasons for the Project Manager *assessing a compensation event*

There are four reasons why a *Project Manager* assesses[120] a compensation event after he has notified to the *Contractor* that he will be doing so:[121]

(1)   The *Contractor* did not submit his quotations and accompanying details in time. The *Contractor* has three weeks to submit quotations after being instructed to do so, or an agreed extended time period.[122]

(2)   The *Project Manager* decides that the *Contractor* has not assessed the event correctly and he does not instruct a revised quotation. The *Project Manager* has the choice of instructing a revised quotation and he would tend to do so only if he thought that the explanation for requesting a revised quotation would yield the required results.

(3)   The *Contractor* has not submitted a required programme with his quotation.[123] If the programme has changed in any way, for example the resource or method statement,[124] or a changed Completion Date (or, in ECC3, a changed Key Date), the *Contractor* must submit a revised programme as part of the compensation event quotation.[125]

(4)   The *Project Manager* has not accepted the *Contractor*'s last programme for a reason stated in the contract by the time the *Contractor* submits the quotation for the compensation event. The *Contractor* is required to submit a revised programme regularly,[126] but if the latest programme submitted has not been accepted by the *Project Manager* for a reason stated in the contract, then the *Project Manager* is entitled to make his own assessment.

The *Contractor* is therefore incentivised to ensure that his programme is submitted as required. A further incentive exists in clause 64.2, where the *Project Manager* assesses[127] a compensation event using his own assessment of the programme if there is no Accepted Programme or if the *Contractor* has not submitted a revised programme[128] for acceptance as required by the contract.

> The programme is so important that its non-acceptance is grounds for the *Project Manager* making his own assessment of compensation events.

1.9.1.2 Procedure for the Project Manager *assessment*

The *Project Manager* has three weeks from the time that the need for the *Project Manager*'s assessment has become apparent[129] to notify the *Contractor* of his assessment of the compensation event and give him details.[130] If the *Contractor* was allowed more than three weeks to submit his quotation, then the *Project Manager* is allowed that same extra time to do his own assessment and notify the *Contractor*.

[120]Note that there is no option for the *Project Manager* to choose not to assess if the reasons exist; the statement is obligatory.
[121]Clause 64.1.
[122]Clauses 62.3 and 62.5.
[123]In ECC3, this has been amended to 'if, when the *Contractor* submits required quotations for a compensation event, he has not submitted a programme or alterations to a programme which this contract requires him to submit'.
[124]Called in ECC3 'a statement of how the *Contractor* plans to do his work'.
[125]Clause 62.2.
[126]Clause 32.2.
[127]Again, there is no option for the *Project Manager*; the action is obligatory.
[128]Changed in ECC3 to 'a programme or alterations to a programme...'.
[129]That is, three weeks from the time the *Project Manager* notified the *Contractor* that he would be making his own assessment.
[130]Clause 64.3.

1.10 The use of the programme for the assessment of compensation events

Like most contracts, there is a relationship between the cost and time effects of change. In the ECC the programme is part of a quotation for a compensation event, which is a package of time and money.

The programme is therefore intrinsically linked with the effects and management of change.

1.10.1 Programmes which accompany compensation events
The same principles which apply to the Accepted Programme apply to programmes which accompany compensation events. Great care is needed when assessing the time effects where the operation or activity has a learning curve.

For instance, a profile of outputs for a tunnelling contract may look like the example given in Fig. 1.2.

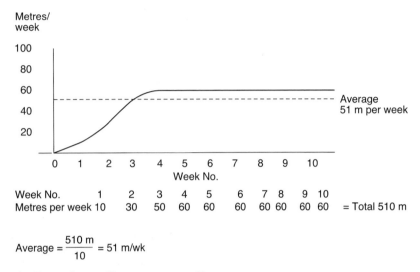

Week No.	1	2	3	4	5	6	7	8	9	10	
Metres per week	10	30	50	60	60	60	60	60	60	60	= Total 510 m

$$\text{Average} = \frac{510\ m}{10} = 51\ m/wk$$

Fig. 1.2. Planned tunnelling progress profile

It can be seen from Fig. 1.2 that the point when the compensation event arises and the time when it is to be undertaken may be at different points on the tunnelling progress profile, and so a compensation event issued shortly after work commences in week 1 to lengthen the tunnel by 20 metres should be based on the planned output rates in week 10 of 60 metres a week and not at the planned output rate of 10 metres per week.

Another example is where the *Contractor* has to construct an escalator box with a hundred secant piles. The *Contractor* commences work and he subsequently advises the *Project Manager* that the first ten piles have taken considerably longer than anticipated due to him encountering physical conditions that an experienced contractor would not have foreseen encountering, namely the ground having unforeseen physical obstructions. It would be wrong at this stage for the *Project Manager* to assume that the next 90 piles would encounter the same conditions and to award a blanket compensation event, covering all 100 piles. Each pile must be taken on its own merits.

It should also be remembered that the failure of the *Contractor* to supply a programme which demonstrates the effects of a compensation event is grounds for the *Project Manager* to make his own assessment of the time effects of the compensation event.

1.11 Implementation of compensation events

This stage represents the formal conclusion of the administrative process.

Implementation of a compensation event takes place in different ways in ECC2 and ECC3.

In ECC2, implementation of a compensation event takes place in one of three ways:[131]

(1)   when the *Project Manager* accepts a quotation,
(2)   when the *Project Manager* completes his own assessment,
(3)   when the compensation event occurs,

whichever is the latest.

Because a compensation event is allowed to be notified if it is expected to happen – that is, the event is still in the future – the entire procedure may have been completed, including the acceptance of a quotation, before the event actually occurs. Implementation therefore takes place when the compensation event occurs since this is the latest happening of the three above.

In ECC3, implementation of a compensation event takes place in one of three ways:

(1)   when the *Project Manager* notifies his acceptance of a quotation,
(2)   when the *Project Manager* notifies the *Contractor* of his own assessment, or
(3)   a *Contractor*'s quotation is treated as having been accepted by the *Project Manager*.

In ECC3, the third manner of implementation occurs where, under clause 61.4, the *Project Manager* does not reply to a compensation event notification by the *Contractor* within two weeks of the notification. In this case, the failure to respond is **deemed to be acceptance** of the compensation event by the *Project Manager*, as well as an instruction to submit quotations. The *Contractor* is advised to quote this clause with his quotation in this instance.

ECC2 takes into account that a compensation event may be notified before it has actually happened, and in this case, implementation would take place only when the compensation event occurs (third manner of implementation described in ECC2). ECC3 does not recognise this and the compensation event would be notified when the quotation is accepted (or when the *Project Manager* makes his own assessment), even if the compensation event has yet to occur.

The acceptance of a quotation is always an alternative to the *Project Manager* doing his own assessment, so the compensation event is implemented when either one occurs, since both cannot happen in the same compensation event.

If

- the *Project Manager* instructed a quotation for a proposed instruction or a proposed changed decision, and if
- he decides as a result of the quotation to give the instruction (or changed decision),

then

- he can either accept the quotation or
- make his own assessment or
- instruct a revised quotation, in which case the revised quotation will either be accepted or assessed by the *Project Manager*.

There are further steps to implementation for each of the main Options.

For Options A, B, C and D,[132] the *Project Manager* includes in his notification implementing a compensation event:

- the changes to the Prices,
- the Completion Date and
- in ECC3, the Key Dates

from the quotation, which he has accepted, or from his own assessment.

---

[131]Clause 65.1.
[132]Clauses A65.4, B65.4, C65.4 and D65.4.

For Options E and F,[133] the *Project Manager* includes the changes to the forecast amount of the Prices and the Completion Date (and, in ECC3, the Key dates) in his notification implementing a compensation event.

1.12 Reduction of Prices

The only compensation events in clause 60.1 which allow a reduction of the Prices (if the assessment shows a reduction in Actual/Defined Cost plus the Fee) are

- a change to the Works Information[134] and
- the correction of an assumption made in assessing an earlier compensation event under clause 61.6.[135]

The only compensation events in the Option clauses which allow a reduction of the Prices are those arising from clauses 60.4 and 60.6 in main Options B and D and from secondary Option clause ECC2 T1 or ECC3 X2.1. All other compensation events listed in clause 60.1 and in the Option clauses cannot lead to reduced Prices even if their effect is to reduce Actual/Defined Cost plus Fee.

There is provision for additional compensation events to be included in the Contract Data. Such additional compensation events can only lead to increased or unchanged Prices unless an additional condition, using secondary Option Z, states specifically that it can also lead to reduced Prices.

1.13 Frequently asked questions

1.13.1 Two-week barrier What happens if the *Contractor* notifies the event more than two weeks after he became aware of it?[136]

(1) The first consideration is how to prove when the *Contractor* became aware of the event. The trigger is not when the event occurred, but when the *Contractor* became aware of it. In most cases, the *Contractor* should be aware immediately, due to a notification or an instruction or some other visible evidence.

(2) The second element to consider is what impact the late notification has had on the project and the *Project Manager*'s ability to manage the project. A late notification could mean that decisions that had been open to the *Project Manager* are now closed due to passage of time and due to superseding events. It could be said that the *Project Manager* has been prejudiced in his ability to manage the project.

(3) Contractually, the *Contractor* has two weeks (eight weeks in ECC3) **only** to notify a compensation event. If notification does not take place within this period then the *Contractor* loses his **contractual** right to compensation. He still retains his legal right to compensation, however. This means that an *Adjudicator* should uphold the two weeks but a court could instruct compensation.

The *Contractor* should not rely on his legal right to relieve him of his contractual duty, however. There is a reason for the two-week barrier and in the interests of the efficacy of the contract and in the interest of the mutual trust and cooperation that underpins the contract, the *Contractor* should endeavour to stick to the two weeks.

Some employers amend clause 61 to make the two weeks a condition precedent for the continuation of the procedure and the entitlement to an assessment of time and money. It could well be argued, however, that such a clause is against the rules of natural justice and justified enrichment. This could be particularly applicable where the *Project Manager* has not carried out

---

[133]Clauses E65.3 and F65.3.
[134]Clause 60.1(1).
[135]Clause 60.1(17).
[136]ECC3: eight weeks.

his actions under the contract, such as notified a compensation event resulting from his own actions. In ECC3, if the *Contractor* does not notify a compensation event within eight weeks of becoming aware of it but the event is a matter that should have been notified to the *Project Manager* as a compensation event and was not, then the *Contractor* does not lose his entitlement to an assessment of time and money. Clause 61.7 of ECC3 states that a compensation event is not notified after the *defects date*. It does not seem to be in the spirit of the NEC to wait until the last minute to notify a quotation, however. See section 1.13.2(4) below.

In conclusion, it is recommended that all the circumstances should be taken into consideration prior to rejecting a compensation event notification. Above all else, mutual trust and cooperation as embodied by fair and reasonable actions is the philosophy of the NEC and to act otherwise could result in unnecessary conflict.

1.13.2 Claims

What happens if the *Contractor* submits a 'claim'-type document?

(1) Where the *Contractor*'s compensation event notification was accepted and he was instructed to submit quotations, a poorly drafted quotation does not detract from the fact that the compensation event has been validly notified and accepted.

(2) The *Project Manager* may choose to make his own assessment; however, this should always be a last resort since not only is it difficult to do, but it may result in a dispute.

(3) The most effective action to take would be to sit with the *Contractor* and go through the *Project Manager*'s expectations of a quotation. In particular, it should be explained that global forecasts are not acceptable and that quotations cannot be revisited after the compensation event has been implemented.

(4) The incidence of claims may increase in ECC3 since the *Contractor* is no longer obliged to notify a compensation event if the *Project Manager* does not. Because there is no time limit on the notification of a compensation event in this case (other than that it must take place before the *defects date*), the *Contractor* may notify the event at Completion, although the event took place much earlier. This is not in the spirit of the NEC, however, nor does it help the *Contractor*'s cash flow and he is advised to notify the event himself.

1.13.3 *Project Manager* does not notify

What happens if the *Project Manager* does not notify a compensation event that he should have done (ECC2 only – see 1.13.2(4) above for ECC3)?

(1) The principle in the NEC is that where the *Employer*, the *Project Manager* or the *Supervisor* do not carry out their obligations, it is a compensation event. Where the *Contractor* is in breach of contract, there is no contractual remedy. This is based on the premise that the *Contractor* is likely to be financially influenced by his own breaches and is therefore less likely to commit them in the first place.

(2) In this case, however, there is no direct sanction on the *Project Manager* for not notifying a compensation event that he should notify. This is possibly because of the inherent failsafe that the *Contractor* may notify the event if the *Project Manager* does not. It is therefore in the *Contractor*'s interests to notify compensation events.

1.13.4 Early warnings

How does an early warning affect a later compensation event on the same matter?

(1) The *Contractor* and the *Project Manager* are both obliged to notify an early warning as soon as either becomes aware of any matter that could:
- increase the total of the Prices,
- in ECC3 delay meeting a Key Date,
- delay Completion or
- impair the performance of the *works* in use.

This is to give the *Contractor* and the *Project Manager* time to consider the implications of the matter and to take action to mitigate any potential consequences.

(2)   If the *Project Manager* decides that the *Contractor* did not notify an early warning that an experienced contractor could have notified and the same matter becomes a compensation event, the *Project Manager* informs the *Contractor* of this decision when he instructs the *Contractor* to submit quotations.

(3)   Notifying the *Contractor* in this way means that the *Contractor* has to assess the compensation event as if he had given the early warning, and it means that the *Project Manager* may assess the compensation event in the same way if he has chosen to assess the event himself.

(4)   The reason for this procedure is to ensure that the *Contractor*'s not notifying an early warning matter does not prejudice the *Project Manager* in his management of the project. If, for example, the matter had been identified, avenues available to the *Project Manager* at that time might have been sufficiently flexible to facilitate the most economical route to have been chosen.

1.13.5 Grouping compensation events

What does the *Project Managers* do if many compensation events take place over a short period of time? Does he have to attend to each separately?

Because the compensation event procedure is fairly long and complex, it is understood that using the procedure for small compensation events that will be carried out in a few hours seems a little arduous.

Many *Project Managers* allow the grouping of smaller compensation events into one notified compensation event on a specified day of the week, for example Friday. All the smaller events that took place during the event are then collected and notified in one compensation event notification. Larger compensation events that require time and effort to assess are still notified separately.

This should only affect Options C and D contracts. Options A and B contracts should not be subject to many compensation events due to the philosophy behind the fixed price required. Compensation events under Option E are mostly important for time purposes rather than budget purposes, although the compensation event quotations are obviously included in the forecast of Actual Cost[137] (budget).

Another, related, matter is where *Contractors* have not correctly forecast the consequential results of a compensation event. This could happen where a relatively minor compensation event of low value has a large consequential impact on the programme. Many *Project Managers* in this situation allow a dummy compensation event that sweeps up the consequential events of previous compensation events.

1.13.6 Amending the contract prior to execution

What does the *Project Manager* do if the drawings change before he has issued the contract? Can he use the compensation event procedure to change the prices to reflect the new drawings?

The compensation event procedure is a part of the contract and since the contract in this situation is not yet in place, it is a little incongruous to be using a contractual procedure to sort out something that is happening before the contract. You can do virtually anything by agreement, however, and if both parties agree to use the tendered data for the Schedule of Cost Components to amend the tendered prices to reflect updated drawings, then this is acceptable. It is probably difficult to check the validity of the quotation, however, given the lack of documentation accompanying a previous event.

More importantly, however, is that fact that the Prices are changed before the contract is executed. As long as you have the time available to make these changes, this is better than issuing an obsolete contract and immediately issuing a score of compensation events.

[137]ECC3 – Defined Cost.

1.13.7 Removing compensation events

Of the 18 compensation events contained in clause 60.1,[138] the two that are most frequently varied are clauses 60.1(12) and 60.1(13); that is, the compensation events that deal with physical conditions and weather.

The basic premise of a compensation event is that the *Employer* takes the risk for the event described. In this way, the risks to be taken by the *Contractor* are clearly laid out and the *Contractor* is able to price the contract effectively, taking into account those elements of the contract that are at his risk. Many employers are so used to writing out ground conditions in an ICE contract that they automatically want to exclude clause 60.1(12) of the ECC as well. It may therefore be worth spending just a little time on the concept of risk and how it affects the contract.

> Risk is not transferred but is reallocated.

One of the principal misconceptions about risk is that it is 'transferable'. Some employers like to use the phrase 'transfer the risk to the contractor'. In general, however, the risk is not 'passed' to the contractor, but rather it takes on a different form and is reallocated. If, for example, in a traditional contract not the ECC, the employer decides that he does not want to take the risk of ground conditions and he rewrites the contract so that the contractor has the risk of ground conditions, the risk has assumed a different form for the employer.

If the contract is a lump sum contract, it is likely that the contractor will build the potential cost of such a risk into the contract price. He might be conservative in his estimate of the occurrence of the risk and so may include a monetary value in the contract price at a high level to cover his risk. This might not even stop him submitting a claim to the engineer if the risk does materialise and the cost to the contractor is far in excess of that included in the contract price. If, on the other hand, the risk does not materialise, all things equal, the contractor will have pocketed the cost of the risk. Whether the risk occurs or not, therefore, the employer will pay.

In a cost-reimbursable-type contract, the employer will pay for the risk whether it is allocated to the contractor or to the employer. It is unlikely that the contractor will accept a risk unconditionally, and perhaps the employer should consider whether it is fair and reasonable that the contractor takes the risk for something that is unforeseen and outwith the contractor's control. In general, therefore, it is more effective for the employer to pay for a risk that does occur, than to pay for something that might happen.

Getting back to the ECC and compensation events, it is worth noting that all the events are well defined. In particular, the two most contentious events, namely physical conditions and weather, are more than simply 'unforeseen ground conditions' or 'inclement weather'. The approach is more objective and therefore more measurable than in traditional contracts.

1.13.8 Adding compensation events

The compensation events contained in the main and secondary Options are optional by virtue of their being part of an Option and therefore these will not be discussed further.

The ECC2 published guidance notes give some elements that may be added as compensation events. A frequent addition is that of wind to the weather compensation event as an additional *weather measurement*. In adding an element, the employer should consider the following:

- What is it that will affect the project? Is it gusts or a constant wind speed above a certain speed?
- What does the Met Office measure and how near to the Site is this measured?

[138]ECC3 19 compensation events.

- Does the *Employer* want to take the risk for this? That is, what will be the effect on the project and who is best placed to manage this risk?
- What is the policy for managing situations where there is no fault?[139]

> Risk should be allocated to the Party best placed to manage it.

It may be that wind is not a *weather measurement* but high-speed gusts of 120 mph blow down a structure. Since wind is not a *weather measurement*, there can be no compensation event, but it is advisable that the *Project Manager* considers the situation anyway and perhaps comes to a commercial settlement. For example, were the winds forecast and did the *Contractor* take what precautions he could in the time allowed to prevent damage? Did the *Employer* facilitate the *Contractor*'s actions? What is the extent of the damage to the project and how will this event affect the rest of the project? It may be in the interests of the project to provide the *Contractor* with the means to very quickly repair the damage so that a critical date is met. Future relations with the *Contractor*, social and environmental responsibilities, and insurances should all also be considered by the *Project Manager*.

1.13.9 The *Project Manager* fails to act   This is one of the most frustrating and difficult things for a *Contractor* to contend with under ECC2. There is no simple answer to this question other than the hope that the *Employer* will employ the right competency of person and that he will recognise when his *Project Manager* is failing to act, and if this is persistent then he will replace him.

The NEC Panel, in reviewing the contract for the 3rd Edition, have taken the opportunity to address this issue (see Table 1.2).

Table 1.2. ECC3 clauses where the *Project Manager* fails to act

Clause	Description
61.3	'…unless the *Project Manager* should have notified the event to the *Contractor* but did not.'
61.4	'…If the *Project Manager* does not notify his decision to the *Contractor* within either • one week of the *Contractor*'s notification or • a longer period to which the *Contractor* has agreed the *Contractor* may notify the *Project Manager* to this effect. A failure by the *Project Manager* to reply within two weeks of this notification is treated as acceptance by the *Project Manager* that the event is a compensation event and an instruction to submit a quotation.'
62.6	'If the *Project Manager* does not reply to a quotation within the time allowed, the *Contractor* may notify the *Project Manager* to this effect…. If the *Project Manager* does not reply to the notification within two weeks, unless the quotation is for a proposed instruction or a proposed changed decision, the *Contractor*'s notification is treated as acceptance of the quotation by the *Project Manager*.'

Those who are operating in collaborative/partnering arrangements may wish to amend the contract to reflect the idea of sanctions against the *Project Manager* for non-performance.

1.14 Format of a compensation event quotation

A quotation for a compensation event comprises

- proposed changes to the Prices and
- any delay to the Completion Date (and Key Dates in ECC3) assessed by the *Contractor*.

[139]This is helped to a certain extent by compensation event 60.1(19) in ECC3.

See Appendix 2 of Chapter 2 for a sample of a compensation event quotation. See Chapter 2 for how to use the Schedule of Cost Components. Appendix 2 of Chapter 2 contains example standard forms that may be used during the compensation event procedure.

Appendix 1 Compensation event procedure

Synopsis

This appendix describes the compensation event procedure through:

- Listing actions to be taken by the *Contractor* and *Project Manager*

- Flow-charting the procedure and

- Drafting a timeline for the compensation procedure notified by both the *Contractor* and the *Project Manager*

Section A – Actions required to be taken by the *Project Manager*

Key:

PM = *Project Manager*
C = *Contractor*
CE = *Compensation event*
S = *Supervisor*

Notifications	Clause	Action
	61.1	PM **notifies** the C of a CE arising from the PM or S giving an instruction or changing an earlier decision.
	61.4	PM **notifies** his decision to the C when he considers that an event notified by the C is not a CE.
	61.5	PM **notifies** his decision to the C that he believes the C did not give an early warning of the CE which an experienced C could have given.
	61.6	PM **notifies** corrections to earlier assumptions upon which he instructed C to base his quotation in cases where effects of CE were too uncertain at time of event.
	62.3	Following submission by the C of a quotation for a CE the PM may **notify** the C that the PM will be making his own assessment (for reasons stated in clause 64).
	62.3	Where the PM has instructed the C to submit a quotation for a **proposed** instruction, following submission of the quotation, the PM may **notify** the C that the proposed instruction will not be given.
	62.5	The PM **notifies** the C of any extensions to the time allowed for either the C to submit quotations or the PM to reply to quotations.
	64.3	Where the PM makes his own assessment of a CE he **notifies** the C of his own assessment.
	65.1	PM implements a CE by **notifying** the C of the quotation which he has accepted or of his own assessment.

Instructions	Clause	Action
	61.1	PM **instructs** the C to submit quotations for CEs arising from the PM or S giving an instruction or changing an earlier decision.
	61.2	PM may **instruct** the C to submit quotations for a proposed instruction or a proposed changed decision.
	61.4	PM **instructs** the C to submit a quotation when he decides that an event notified by the C is a CE.
	62.1	PM may **instruct** the C to submit alternative quotations based upon different ways of dealing with CE.
	62.3/4	Following submission by the C of a quotation for a CE the PM **instructs** the C to submit a revised quotation.

Acceptances	Clause	Action
	62.3	Following submission by the C of a quotation for a CE the PM **accepts** the quotation.

Section B – Actions required to be taken by the *Contractor*

Key:

PM	=	*Project Manager*
C	=	*Contractor*
CE	=	Compensation event
S	=	*Supervisor*

Notifications	Clause	Action
	61.3	For CEs not notified by the PM, the C **notifies** the PM why he considers that the CE has happened or is expected to happen.

Submissions	Clause	Action
	62.3	C **submits** quotations for CEs.
	62.4	C **submits** revised quotations for CEs.

Section C – Compensation event procedure

*ECC3 states that if the Contractor does not notify an event within eight weeks of becoming aware of the event, he is not entitled to changes in the Prices, Completion Date or Key Date unless the Project Manager should have notified the event to the Contractor but did not.

Section C – Compensation event procedure (continued)

Contractor submits quotations within 3 weeks unless the *PM* and the *Contractor* agree to an extension before the quotation is due. Quotation includes

- other methods of dealing with the event that are practicable
- details of the assessment
- revised programme if the programme is affected
- proposed changes to the Prices and any delay to the Completion Date (ECC3: and the Key Dates)

PM replies within 2 weeks unless *PM* and *Contractor* agree to extension before the reply is due

PM replies

- *Contractor* did not submit quotation in time
- *Contractor* has not assessed CE correctly
- *Contractor* has not submitted required programme
- *PM* has not accepted *Contractor*'s latest programme

PM accepts quotation

PM gives notification that a proposed instruction or proposed changed decision will not be given

PM instructs a revised quotation

PM gives notification that he will be doing his own assessment

3 weeks or longer if the *Contractor* had longer to submit his quotation

PM implements the compensation event

Procedure ends

3 weeks

Contractor submits revised quotation

PM notifies *Contractor* of his assessment and gives details

Procedure ends

PM replies in 2 weeks unless extended

PM implements the compensation event

Procedure ends

Section D – Procedure for events notified by the *Project Manager*

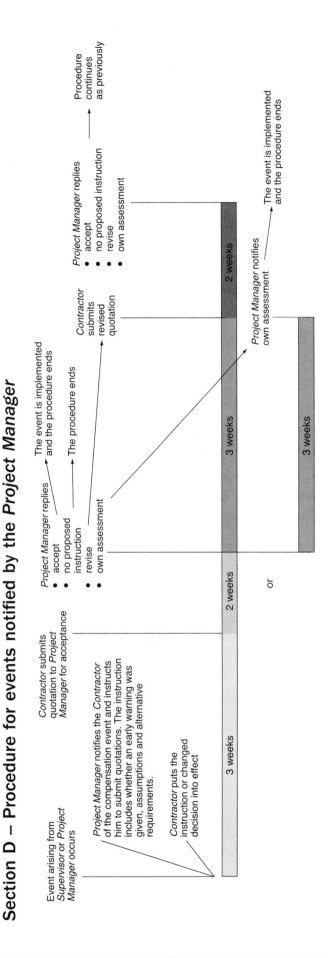

Section E – Procedure for events notified by the Contractor

Contractor notifies event to *Project Manager* if
- is < 2 weeks
- it is a CE
- the PM has not notified it

Event occurs

Project Manager decides whether the event passes the four-point test and either
- notifies his decision that the procedure ends if the event fails the test or
- instructs the *Contractor* to submit quotations

Contractor submits quotations

Project Manager replies
- accept
- no proposed instruction
- revise
- own assessment

The event is implemented and the procedure ends

The procedure ends

Contractor submits revised quotation

Project Manager replies
- accept
- no proposed instruction
- revise
- own assessment

Project Manager notifies own assessment

The event is implemented and the procedure ends

2* weeks | 1 week | 3 weeks | 2 weeks | 3 weeks | 2 weeks

3 weeks

* ECC3 states that if the *Contractor* does not notify an event within eight weeks of becoming aware of the event, he is not entitled to changes in the Prices, Completion Date or Key Date unless the *Project Manager* should have notified the event to the *Contractor* but did not.

Section F – Most common complicating factors

Key:

C	=	*Contractor*
PM	=	*Project Manager*
A	=	*Adjudicator*
CE	=	Compensation event

Complicating factor	Action required	Further possible action
PM decides that an event notified by C as a CE is not a CE [61.4]	C may notify PM of his intention to submit dispute to A [90.1 or ECC3: W1.1 or W2.1]	PM within two weeks of C's notification changes decision previously communicated to C and instructs C to submit a quotation [60.1(8), 61.4] OR PM does not change decision previously communicated to C and risk C submitting dispute to A
C fails to submit a quotation and details of his assessment within three weeks or other extended period agreed [62.3]	PM assesses the CE and notifies C of his assessment within same period originally allowed to C for submission [64.1, 64.3]	C may notify PM of his intention to submit dispute to A if he believes PM's assessment to be incorrectly calculated [90.1 or ECC3: W1.1 or W2.1]
PM believes the C has not assessed the CE correctly in a quotation submitted	PM instructs the C to submit a revised quotation explaining his reasons for doing so [62.4] OR PM assesses the CE and notifies C of his assessment [64.1, 64.3]	C resubmits quotation [62.4] OR C may notify PM of his intention to submit dispute to A if he believes PM's reasons to be ill judged [90.1 or ECC3: W1.1 or W2.1] OR C may notify PM of his intention to submit dispute to A if he believes PM's assessment to be incorrectly calculated [90.1 or ECC3: W1.1 or W2.1]

2 Schedule of Cost Components

Synopsis

This chapter discusses aspects relating to the Schedule of Cost Components, including:

- When the Schedule of Cost Components (SCC) is used

- How the SCC interacts with the payment clauses

- Actual Cost and Defined Cost

- The Fee

- The components of cost Included under the Schedule of Cost Components

- Contract Data part two

2.1 Introduction

The ECC in common with other standard forms of construction contracts provides rules for assessing:

- The amount to be paid to the *Contractor* for work done, and
- The change to amounts to be paid to the *Contractor* for variations and other events that may arise and which, under the contract, are at the *Employer*'s risk, collectively termed compensation events by the ECC.

Depending on which of the Main Options A to E the *Employer* chooses, the Schedule of Cost Components (SCC) is central to one or both of the above assessments.

Given then its obvious connection to the financial outcome of a contract it is perhaps unfortunate that the SCC has so far proven to be one of the least understood parts of the ECC. This chapter therefore sets out to examine the purpose and detail of the SCC using examples and discussion to provide a better understanding of this fundamentally important part of the ECC.

2.2 What is the Schedule of Cost Components?

To understand the role of the SCC in the administration of the contract we need to first identify where it is referred to in the contract.

A search reveals that the only reference to it occurs in the definition of Actual Cost.[140] Since the definition of Actual Cost[141] differs depending on which main Option of the ECC is used, it is to the main Option clauses that we must turn.

It has been stated that the principal role of the main Option clauses is to determine how the *Contractor* is to be reimbursed for his efforts or, expressed more formally, where the financial risk boundary is set between *Employer* and *Contractor* (refer to Chapter 2 of Book 2). This immediately establishes that the role of the SCC must be linked to how the *Contractor* is reimbursed.

To confuse matters a little in this area there are in fact two SCCs, namely:

(1)   the Schedule of Cost Components, often referred to by practitioners as the 'full' Schedule of Cost Components, and
(2)   the Shorter Schedule of Cost Components.

What follows relates to the full SCC, since an understanding of this will make it far easier to understand the differences between the use and content of the two schedules.

The Schedule of Cost Components is a complete identification of the components of cost for which the *Contractor* will be reimbursed under certain circumstances. These components of cost are a part of Actual Cost[142] as defined.

The term Actual Cost[143] could be confusing since it does not mean actual cost as we would understand it in everyday language of meaning all costs. Instead it is defined and includes the components in the Schedule of Cost Components.

It is important to note that the definition of Actual Cost[144] differs dependent upon which of the six main Options, A to F is being used.

These components of cost are **not priced at the time of tender**. However, in Contract Data part two the *Contractor* is required to insert certain information in relation to these components of cost.

---

[140]ECC3 Defined Cost.
[141]ECC3 Defined Cost.
[142]ECC3 Defined Cost.
[143]This term always raised discussion and this is why in ECC3 it has been changed to Defined Cost.
[144]ECC3 Defined Cost.

> The Schedule of Cost Components is a complete identification of the components of cost. The definition of Actual Cost (ECC3 Defined Cost) does not mean all of the *Contractor*'s costs, but is confined to the components as listed in the Schedule of Cost Components.
>
> The definition of Actual Cost (ECC3 Defined Cost) differs dependent upon which of the six main Options you are using.
>
> The SCC is NOT PRICED at the time of tender.
>
> Contract Data part two contains information required for use in conjunction with the Schedule of Cost Components. It is therefore VERY IMPORTANT that this is completed correctly at the time of tender.

2.3 Why has this approach been taken?

Traditionally, the valuation of change has been assessed on the basis of tendered rates and prices. Problems occur, however, when, as often happens on projects, the scope and nature of the project start to vary and arguments then arise with regard to the applicability of bills of quantities rates, prices and lump sum items and how much the quantity/type/scope of an item needs to change before a new rate or price is required.

It is possible to argue ad infinitum about the rights and wrongs of a particular price. The Schedule of Cost Components is a way around these problems.

The ECC promotes the idea of the pre-assessment of change via a quotation. This supports the concept of 'stimulus to good management'.[145] A well-run project will identify change at the earliest time possible. This supports the idea that 'foresight applied collaboratively mitigates problems and shrinks risk'.[146]

In the ECC all change is valued at 'Actual Cost'[147] with no reference made to tendered rates or prices.[148] The philosophy behind this provision is that the *Contractor* should be 'no better nor no worse off' as a result of change which is at the risk of the *Employer* under the contract during the construction of the *works*.

This approach also enables the *Employer* to call for quotations for a number of options on how to deal with the change. Therefore if the *Employer* has a facility to be opened by a certain date or costs are of paramount importance, then the *Employer* can consider and instruct the *Contractor* to submit quotations for these options.

The *Contractor* is conceptually in the same position when pricing the quotation, as he would have been at the time of tender. He also, as with tendering, carries the risk should his quotation be wrong.

> The idea with the SCC is that conceptually the *Contractor* is in the same position for a compensation event as when he tenders for the work.

2.4 Assessment options

The default situation for assessing the changes to the Prices is the full SCC. However, there is an option to use:

- the Shorter Schedule of Cost Components (Shorter SCC) for simple changes or
- rates, prices and lump sums in the *bills of quantities* by agreement in main Options B and D.

We will look at these alternatives in more detail later in the chapter.

[145]The ECC2 Engineering and Construction Contract Guidance Notes page 2.
[146]The ECC2 Engineering and Construction Contract Guidance Notes page 3.
[147]ECC3 Defined Cost.
[148]Except Options B and D ECC2 clause 63.9; ECC3 clause 63.13, A63.14, B63.13, D63.13.

2.5 When is the Schedule of Cost Components used?

The Schedule of Cost Components has the following uses in the ECC main Options:

- It defines the cost components for which the *Contractor* will be directly reimbursed for **non-subcontracted work** (Options C, D and E).
- It defines those cost elements which are admissible in any assessment of the changes to the Prices as a result of compensation events (Options A, B, C, D and E).[149]

2.5.1 Priced-based contracts – Options A and B contracts

Options A and B are the priced-based Options (lump sum and remeasurable respectively). The definition of the Price for Work Done to Date under these options is based on the *activity schedule* and the *bill of quantities* respectively rather than on Actual Cost.[150] Therefore under these main Options the full Schedule of Cost Components (FSCC) or the Shorter Schedule of Cost Components (SSCC) is used to evaluate compensation events only.[151]

Option A – payment during the contract

For Option A contracts, the *Contractor* is reimbursed using the *activity schedule* for his work carried out during the period of the contract and priced at tender stage. That is, the *Contractor* is paid the lump sum price listed in the *activity schedule* when that activity is completed. Each completed activity then forms part of what is termed the Price for Work Done to Date.[152]

Option A – evaluating compensation events

The financial effects of all compensation events that occur during the period of the contract are not priced using lump sum prices in the *activity schedule* as a basis, but using the SCC.[153] That is, any additional costs arising under the contract, including additional Subcontractor costs, are quoted for using the Schedule of Cost Components.

The accepted compensation events are added to the lump sum Prices in the *activity schedule* and the *Contractor* is therefore paid for the compensation events through the mechanism of the Price for Work Done to Date.

> **Option A**
>
> The lump sum prices inserted by the *Contractor* at the tender stage for each activity on the *activity schedule* are not used to assess the financial effect of compensation events.
>
> The FSCC (not used in ECC3) and SSCC are only used for the assessment of change to the Prices as a result of compensation events.
>
> Tendered rates and prices are NOT USED to assess change.

Option B – payment during the contract

For Option B contracts, the *Contractor* is reimbursed using the *bill of quantities* for his work carried out during the period of the contract and priced at tender stage.

Option B – evaluating compensation events

The financial effects of compensation events that occur during the period of the contract are not priced using the rates and prices in the *bill of quantities* as a basis, but using the SCC.[154] This is the default position described in the contract and may discourage possible front loading of the bill rates and prices impacting on costs. However, for Option B contracts, the *Project Manager* and the *Contractor*

---

[149]ECC3 only the Shorter Schedule of Cost Components is used for Options A and B.
[150]ECC3 Defined Cost.
[151]ECC3 only Shorter Schedule of Cost Components used to assess compensation events.
[152]ECC2 clause 11.2(24); ECC3 clause 11.2(27).
[153]ECC3 only the Shorter SCC may be used.
[154]ECC3 only the Shorter SCC may be used.

may decide to use the SSCC[155] or rates in the *bills of quantities*[156] instead of the SSCC to calculate the cost of compensation events.[157]

Option B

The rates, prices and lump sums inserted by the *Contractor* at tender stage for each *bills of quantities* item are not used to assess the financial effects of compensation events.

The FSCC (ECC2 only) is only used for the assessment of change to the Prices as a result of compensation events.

By agreement, the SSCC or rates in the *bills of quantities* can be used to assess the financial effects of compensation events.

(ECC2 clause 63.9, ECC3 clause 63.13.)

2.5.2 Cost-based contracts – Options C, D and E contracts

In addition to its use for assessing the financial effect of compensation events under Options C, D or E contracts, the SCC is also used as the basis for calculating the amount due to the *Contractor*.

Options C and D – target cost

The *activity schedule* (for Option C) or *bill of quantities* (for Option D) that is priced by the *Contractor* at tender stage is included in the contract only to provide the target cost.[158] This target cost may be changed through compensation events ('in accordance with this contract').[159] The Prices are only considered during the contract:

- to account for changes through compensation events to ensure that the base comparison of the target cost remains realistic and
- as a comparison with the Price for Work Done to Date to assess the *Contractor*'s share.

The Prices are not used to pay the *Contractor* during the period of the contract and this definition will therefore not be considered further in this chapter. For a fuller discussion of target cost and the *Contractor*'s share, see Chapter 2 of Book 2 on contract options.

Options C, D and E – payment during the contract and the evaluation of compensation events

The Price for Work Done to Date is effectively the amount due[160] to the *Contractor* as assessed by the *Project Manager*. The Price for Work Done to Date (PWDD) is therefore the amount paid to the *Contractor* during the period of the contract. The PWDD is not related to the Prices except where the Prices are used as a comparison against the PWDD to determine the *Contractor*'s share (Options C and D).

The SCC is therefore the only method[161] for the *Contractor* to be reimbursed his costs under Option C, D or E contracts. The exception to this is that under Option D, the *Project Manager* and the *Contractor* may decide to use the rates and prices in the *bill of quantities* to calculate the cost of compensation events instead of the SCC.[162] If the *Project Manager* and the *Contractor* decide, the SSCC can be used to evaluate compensation events instead of the FSCC.[163]

---

[155]ECC3 only the Shorter SCC may be used.
[156]For ECC2 and rates and lump sums in ECC3.
[157]ECC2 clause B63.9; ECC3 clause 63.13.
[158]The Prices as defined in clause ECC2 C11.2(20), ECC3 C11.2(30) and clause ECC2 D11.2(21), ECC3 clause D11.2(31).
[159]ECC2 clause C11.2(20); ECC3 C11.2(30).
[160]Clause 50.2.
[161]Whether FSCC or SSCC – ECC2 clauses C, D, E63.11; ECC3 clauses C, D, E63.15.
[162]ECC2 clause D63.9; ECC3 clause D63.13.
[163]ECC2 clauses C, D and E63.11; ECC3 clauses C, D and E63.15.

Fig. 2.1. Example of the amount due for main Options C, D and E

The PWDD comprises a number of elements as shown in Fig. 2.1.

> **Options C and D**
>
> The lump sum prices inserted by the *Contractor* at the tender stage for each activity on the *activity schedule* or *bills of quantities* are not used to assess the financial effects of compensation events.
>
> The SCC is used to assess compensation events and to determine the Price for Work Done to Date.
>
> Where agreed between the Parties, the SSCC and rates and prices in the *bills of quantities* can also be used to assess the financial effects of compensation events.
>
> Tendered rates and prices are NOT USED to assess the financial effects of compensation events.
>
> **Option E**
>
> The SCC is used to assess both the financial effects of compensation events and to determine the Price for Work Done to Date by the *Contractor*.
>
> Where agreed between the parties, the SSCC can also be used to assess the financial effects of compensation events.

2.5.3 Option F contracts The SCC is not used at all in Option F contracts since the management *Contractor* is paid the amounts due to Subcontractors.[164,165] The assumption is that the management *Contractor* does not do any of the work himself and therefore does not need to be reimbursed in a manner such as that described by the SCC. Where the *Contractor* does do work himself he is paid the lump sum stated in Contract Data part two (ECC3 only).

[164]ECC2 clause F11.2(26); ECC3 clause F11.2(24).
[165]ECC3 and *prices* for work done by the *Contractor* himself.

Table 2.1. Summary of the uses of the SCC for each of the main Options

Main Option	Contract type	Evaluation of the financial effects of compensation events	Payment
A	Priced-based	ECC2: FSCC or SSCC ECC3 SSCC only; or rates and lump sums	Completed activities in the *activity schedule*
B		ECC2: FSCC or SSCC or rates and prices in *bills of quantities* ECC3: SSCC only; or rates and lump sums	*bills of quantities* items multiplied by the rate
C	Cost-based	FSCC or SSCC	FSCC
D		ECC2: FSCC or SSCC or rates and prices in *bills of quantities* ECC3: FSCC or SSCC or rates and lump sums	FSCC
E		FSCC or SSCC	FSCC
F	Management contract	SCC does not apply	Amount of payments to Subcontractors (and in ECC3 the *prices* for work done by the *Contractor* himself)

2.5.4 SCC summary Table 2.1 summarises the use of the full Schedule of Cost Components and Shorter SCC for the six main Options.

> The SCC is used for the assessment of change for main Options A, B, C, D and E.
> (ECC3 FSCC only applies to Options C, D and E.)
>
> The SCC is used for payment on main Options C, D and E.

2.6 ECC2 Actual Cost; ECC3 Defined Cost

In each of the main Options, a clause exists which provides a definition of 'Actual Cost' (ECC3 Defined Cost). A summary of the definitions is shown in Table 2.2.

From Table 2.2 it can be seen that Actual Cost[166] is defined by the Schedule of Cost Components, which provides a list of the components of cost to which the *Contractor* is entitled. This includes such items as wages and salaries and the listed components of the cost of Equipment and Plant and Materials. This is different from some other conditions of contract, where 'actual cost' is used but not defined clearly and objectively.

> The definition of Actual Cost (ECC3 Defined Cost) differs depending upon which of the main Options you are using. You need to look at the particular main Option clauses to determine how to assess changes and how to assess the amount due.

2.7 The Fee

All the costs to the *Contractor* not covered under the SCC are deemed to be covered by the Fee.[167] The Fee is calculated by multiplying the *fee*

[166]ECC3 Defined Cost.
[167]Clause 52.1.

Table 2.2. Definition of Actual/Defined Cost for the six main Options

Main Option	Clause ref.	Definition of Actual/Defined Cost[168]
A	ECC2 11.2(28)	Actual Cost is the cost of components in the Schedule of Cost Components whether work is subcontracted or not, excluding the cost of preparing quotations for compensation events.
	ECC3 11.2(22)	Defined Cost is the cost of the components in the Shorter Schedule of Cost Components whether work is subcontracted or not, excluding the cost of preparing quotations for compensation events.
B	ECC2 11.2(28)	As Option A.
	ECC3 11.2(22)	As Option A.
C	ECC2 11.2(27)	Amount of payments due to Subcontractors for work subcontracted and the cost of components in Schedule of Cost Components for work not subcontracted, less any Disallowed Cost.

	ECC3 11.2(23)	Defined Cost is:
		• the amounts of payments due to Subcontractors for work which is subcontracted without taking account of amounts deducted for
		  • retention
		  • payment to the *Employer* as a result of the Subcontractor failing to meet a Key Date
		  • the correction of Defects after Completion
		  • payment to Others and
		  • the supply of equipment, supplies and services included in the charge for overhead cost within the Working Areas in this contract
		and
		• the cost of components in the Schedule of Cost Components for other work
		less Disallowed Cost.

D	ECC2 11.2(27)	As Option C
	ECC3 11.2(23)	As Option C
E	ECC2 11.2(27)	As Option C
	ECC3 11.2(23)	As Option C
F	ECC2 11.2(26)	Amount of payments due to Subcontractors for work which the *Contractor* is required to subcontract, less any Disallowed Cost.

	ECC3 11.2(24)	Defined Cost is:
		• the amounts of payments due to Subcontractors for work which is subcontracted without taking account of amounts deducted for
		  • retention
		  • payment to the *Employer* as a result of the Subcontractor failing to meet a Key Date
		  • the correction of Defects after Completion
		  • payment to Others
		  • the supply of equipment, supplies and services included in the charge for overhead cost within the Working Areas in this contract
		and
		• the *prices* for work done by the *Contractor* himself
		less Disallowed Cost.

[168]Note that Actual/Defined Cost is used only to calculate changes in main Options A and B, but used for all payments in Options C, D and E.

percentage[169] tendered by the *Contractor* in Contract Data part two, with Actual Cost,[170] which is the total of the components of cost as listed in the SCC.

ECC2:   Fee = *fee percentage* × Actual Cost

ECC3:   Fee = (*subcontracted fee percentage*

× Defined Cost of subcontracted work)

+ (*direct fee percentage* × Defined Cost of other work)

The *fee percentage* (ECC3 *direct fee percentage*) should therefore cover:

(1)   the *Contractor*'s desired profit,
(2)   overheads that cannot be claimed as a component of cost in the SCC, meaning head office overheads, since 'site overheads' or 'preliminaries' are generally covered in the SCC.

Examples of inclusions in the *fee percentage* (ECC3 *direct fee percentage*) are as follows:

- profit,
- head office charges and overheads, but not the cost of design by the *Contractor* works which may only be carried out away from the Working Areas – this is a separate cost component in the SCC (unless specified for design, manufacture or fabrication through overhead percentages inserted in Contract Data part two),
- corporation tax, insurance premiums. It should be noted that employer's liability insurance comes under the people cost component in the SCC,
- advertising and recruitment costs,
- sureties and guarantees for the contract.

The *fee percentage* (ECC3 *direct fee percentage*) should exclude that element of the overheads which will be recovered under the manufacture and fabrication and design outside of the Working Areas percentages inserted by the *Contractor* in Contract Data part two.

Table 2.3 shows how a *fee percentage* (ECC3 *direct fee percentage*) might be calculated. The table shows a breakdown of costs, which we can assume has been derived for the *Contractor*'s most recent profit and loss account or from his projections for the current financial year. It is assumed that the company undertakes construction, design and manufacture and fabrication. Column A gives a description of the overhead items. Columns C, D and E split the over-head costs into head office, design and manufacture and fabrication. Column B shows total costs for the whole business.

Figure 2.2 shows the overall breakdown of the *Contractor*'s overheads into head office,[171] manufacture and fabrication and design based on the total overhead burden of £1,700,000.00, as shown in Table 2.3.

It should be borne in mind that the overheads can be a combination of internal/external or a combination of design and manufacture and fabrication. The *Contractor* may need to insert more than one percentage as he may have both internal and external designers who will have different design overheads.

2.7.1 ECC3 *fee percentage*   In ECC3 the Fee[172] is the sum of the amounts calculated by applying:

- the *subcontracted fee percentage* to the Defined Cost of subcontracted work and
- the *direct fee percentage* to the Defined Cost of other work.

---

[169]ECC3 *direct fee percentage* and *subcontracted fee percentage*.
[170]ECC3 Defined Cost.
[171]Where head office overhead of £1,107,000 is 55.35% of the total £2,000,000 overhead (see Table 2.3).
[172]ECC3 clause 11.2(8).

Table 2.3. Fee percentage, design and manufacture and fabrication overheads

Item A	Total overheads B	Head office C	Design office D	Fabrication shop E
Overhead item				
Salaries/wages	7,000,000	700,000	200,000*	100,000*
Rent and rates	175,000	100,000	25,000	50,000
Heating and lighting	35,000	20,000	5,000	10,000
Insurances	115,000	100,000	10,000	5,000
Cleaning	8,000	5,000	1,000	2,000
Stationery/stamps/postage	24,000	12,000	10,000	2,000
Equipment	120,000	50,000	20,000	50,000
Telephone	23,000	20,000	2,000	1,000
Other items	432,500	90,000	5,000	337,500
Shortfall on people costs (see Appendix 3 for a discussion on these issues)	67,500	10,000	20,000	37,500
Total (see Fig. 2.2)	**1,700,000** (100%)	**1,107,000** (62.12%)	**98,000** (5.76%)	**495,000** (29.12%)
Turnover	11,760,000	10,260,000	500,000	1,000,000
Overheads as a % of turnover	14.46%	10.79%	19.6%	49.5%
Add Profit	5%	5%	5%	5%
Percentages for insertion in Contract Data part two	19.45% NOT USED	15.79% fee percentage (ECC3 *direct fee percentage*)	24.6%[173] Design overheads	54.5%[174] Manufacture and fabrication overheads

*Note: These costs are recovered through rates and prices inserted in Contract Data part two.

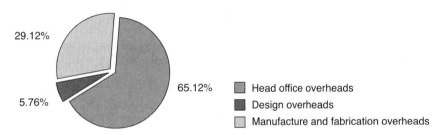

Fig. 2.2. Example of *Contractor*'s overhead breakdown

The Fee in ECC3 now has two components, one for direct work undertaken directly by the *Contractor* and one for the work undertaken by Subcontractors.

This change has been made to overcome the issues regarding the declaration at the time of tender by the *Contractor* of one *fee percentage* to cover his own and the work of his Subcontractors. This caused a few headaches, especially on Options A and B for priced-based contracts where the one *fee percentage* was deemed to cover both the *Contractor*'s direct work and the work of his Subcontractors.

[173]Note that the profit element for any design taking place outside the Working Areas is not added to the design overhead percentage. Profit is included in the *fee percentage* and is therefore added to Actual Cost (ECC3 Defined Cost) through the addition of the Fee. If the profit element of design were to be included in the design overhead percentage, then profit would be received through the design overhead percentage and again through the Fee, giving the *Contractor* more than his usual profit. The design overhead percentage is for overheads only, as indicated in the name.
[174]See footnote 175.

2.8 The components of cost included under the full SCC

The Schedule of Cost Components defines the cost components for which the *Contractor* will be reimbursed for non-subcontracted work (Options C, D and E).[175]

As a general policy the Schedule of Cost Components only provides for the direct reimbursement of those cost components that are readily identifiable. In ECC3 the last sentence of the opening paragraph to the SCC has been changed to reinforce this: 'An amount is included only in one cost component and only if it is incurred in order to Provide the Works.' The principal way that this is achieved is by creating the concept of the Working Areas. Working Areas under an ECC means the areas of land comprising the Site as made available by the *Employer*, together with any additional areas proposed by the *Contractor*[176] and accepted by the *Project Manager* as being necessary to Provide the Works.

Generally, it is only the cost of People and Equipment working within these Working Areas that is reimbursed as Actual Cost.[177] This recognises the difficulty and therefore the higher risk to the *Employer* in identifying and controlling costs that are incurred away from the Site – that is, outside the Working Areas.

The exception to this general principle is those costs incurred by the *Contractor* associated with the design and manufacture and fabrication, outside of the Working Areas which are dealt with in separate cost components 5 and 6 in the SCC.

Recognising that there could be some overlap between various cost components, the Schedule of Cost Components sensibly reminds that 'amounts are included only in one cost component'.[178] The SCC provides for both the direct reimbursement GBP (or other currency) – for (i.e. GBP or other currency) and also for indirect reimbursement, by the use of predetermined percentages to cover a range of cost components.

To make them fully effective they do however require certain data to be inserted by the *Contractor* in Contract Data part two. It is important that all data required by Contract Data part two for both the full and Shorter SCC is inserted by the *Contractor* **before submitting his tender**, since the decision to use one or the other arises during the contract by agreement between the *Contractor* and the *Project Manager*[179] rather than before the contract starts.

There are seven headings for the components of cost included in the SCC:

(1)   People,
(2)   Equipment,
(3)   Plant and Materials,
(4)   Charges,
(5)   Manufacture and fabrication outside the Working Areas,
(6)   Design (outside the Working Areas),
(7)   Insurance.

Under each of these headings are described all the components of cost for which the *Contractor* will be reimbursed during the period of the contract (for Options C, D and E) and which will also be taken into consideration when evaluating the financial effects of compensation events (Options A, B, C, D and E).[180] Any other components of cost not identified in the schedule should be covered and are deemed anyway to be covered by included in the *fee percentage*[181] (ECC3 *direct fee percentage*).

[175]It also defines the cost components which are included in an assessment of changed costs arising from a compensation event (Options A, B, C, D and E). ECC3 SSCC not used to assess change for Options A and B.
[176]In Contract Data part two and through clause 15.1.
[177]ECC3 Defined Cost.
[178]As stated in the preface to the Schedule of Cost Components on page 49 of the ECC2 and page 56 of ECC3.
[179]ECC2 clause 63.11 for Options A, B, C, D, E; ECC3 clause 63.15 for Options C, D and E; ECC3 Options A and B do not use the full SCC.
[180]ECC3: full SCC not used for assessing change in Options A and B.
[181]Clause 52.1.

> In ECC3:
>
> The full SCC only applies to main Options C, D and E.
>
> The introduction to the full SCC has been amended to read as follows:
>
> 'This schedule is part of the *conditions of contract* only when Option C, D or E is used. In this schedule the *Contractor* means the *Contractor* and not his Subcontractors. An amount is included only in one cost component and only if it is incurred in order to Provide the Works.'

2.8.1 Working Areas   Note that except for cost component headings 5 and 6, the components in the Schedule of Cost Components are all for costs within the Working Areas. This means that the identification of the *working areas* by the *Contractor* in Contract Data part two is particularly important. The *working areas* are generally identified as the Site and other areas adjacent or near to the Site that the *Contractor* considers he might use temporarily for the purpose of Providing the Works. Examples are 'borrow pits' or a concrete batching facility established. These should be identified as *working areas*.

A question often asked by *Contractors* is that at tender stage they do not know precisely where the 'borrow pit' will be as they are still in negotiation with land owners and the like. In these circumstances it is important to identify in the Contract Data that you intend to have such a location, even though you may only be able to provide a generic description without a precise location.

2.8.2 Cost component heading 1: People   The full and the Shorter SCC both use the same method for calculating the cost of people, although the actual components of cost described in clauses 11, 12[182] and 13[183] are fewer in the Shorter SCC.

The cost components for people in both the full and the Shorter SCC comprise the following three categories:

Category 1   *Components for 11, 12[184] and 13[185] for people directly employed by the Contractor and whose normal place of working is within the Working Areas.*
(Direct employees of the Contractor whose normal place of working is within the Working Areas, e.g. tradesmen, site agent.)

Category 2   *Components for 11, 12[186] and 13[187] for people directly employed by the Contractor and whose normal place of working is NOT within the Working Areas, but who are working within the Working Areas for a period of not less than one week.*
(Direct employees of the Contractor whose normal place of working is **not** within the Working Areas but who are working in the Working Areas for a [continuous] period of not less than one week, e.g. a specialised tradesman who is used for a compensation event lasting one week.)
In ECC3 this category has been reworded and the requirement for direct employees whose normal place of working is not the Working Areas to work for a [continuous] period of not less than one week has been deleted. Instead they will be paid for the time they are working in the Working Areas.

Category 3   *Components for 11, 12[188] and 13[189] for people who are NOT directly employed by the Contractor, but are paid by the Contractor according to the time worked while they are within the Working Areas.*

[182]ECC3 component 12 is deleted in the SSCC.
[183]ECC3 component 13 is deleted in the SSCC.
[184]ECC3 component 12 is deleted in the SSCC.
[185]ECC3 component 13 is deleted in the SSCC.
[186]ECC3 component 12 is deleted in the SSCC.
[187]ECC3 component 13 is deleted in the SSCC.
[188]ECC3 component 12 is deleted in the SSCC.
[189]ECC3 component 13 is deleted in the SSCC.

(People who are not directly employed by the *Contractor* [and who are not Subcontractors as defined], but are paid by the *Contractor* according to the time worked while they are within the Working Areas, e.g. consultants.)

In ECC3 this category is now included under item 14 and reads:

'14   The following components of the cost of people who are not directly employed by the *Contractor* but are paid for by him according to the time worked while they are within the Working Areas.
Amounts paid by the *Contractor*.'

The inclusion of this category as a new item 14 recognises the problems that the *Contractor* may have in obtaining a breakdown of the costs of category 3 people in ECC2, broken down in the components listed in items 11, 12 and 13 from people not directly employed by the *Contractor*. The words 'Amounts paid' reflect the more normal practice of paying such people on agreed hourly or daily rates.

The words 'Amounts paid by the *Contractor*' may lead to the assumption that whatever the *Contractor* pays, the *Employer* is liable to pay. However, one needs to remember that in ECC3 the FSCC only applies to main Options C, D and E, and that this cost component will therefore come under the scrutiny of clause 11.2(25) Disallowed Cost.

The term 'people' as used by the ECC encompasses the *Contractor*'s staff as well as his labour working within the Working Areas.

The cost of people who are directly employed by the *Contractor* in providing the works but working outside the Working Areas, for example *Contractor*'s staff whose normal place of working is head office, factory, design office or manufacturing facility, are included either in:

- SCC 5 (manufacture and fabrication outside the Working Areas) or in
- SCC 6 (design outside the Working Areas) or in
- the *fee percentage* (ECC3 *direct fee percentage*).

In general, therefore, the cost of the people who are based at Site is a cost component in the SCC. Supporting time sheets or daily labour records would show the amount of time the supervision staff has spent on each project. This is particularly applicable where the *Contractor* is involved in more than one project at the same Site.

There are no direct entries for people required for Contract Data part two since any application for payment would include:

- a payroll printout showing the required information,
- proof of other payments such as lodging allowances,
- other documentary evidence such as invoices for category 3 above.

The payroll printout would be supported by daily labour records and time sheets so that an audit would reveal a fully traceable cost line. See section 2.12 and Appendix 3 of Book 2 for information about audits.

2.8.2.1 Shorter Schedule of Cost Components   In ECC2, categories 11, 12 and 13 are still used, but they are considerably shorter.

In ECC3 the cost component has been simplified to one component 11 rather than the three given in ECC2, as follows:

'11   Amounts paid by the *Contractor* including those for meeting the requirements of the law and for pension provisions.'

This is a far broader term and it would indicate that this component can include the same items as those for the people element in the full SCC.

To these cost components is added a percentage for people overheads see section 2.8.5.2.

2.8.3 Cost component heading 2: Equipment

Equipment is a defined term in the contract and comprises items provided by the *Contractor* that are used to Provide the Works, but not included in the *works*.[190] The term therefore covers a broad range of items, the two obvious categories being construction plant and temporary works. Examples are JCBs, dumpers and generators, scaffolding and temporary sheet piling and formwork.

Note that in ECC2 some items of Equipment such as cabins, computers, hand tools are included under heading 4 Charges, and the *Contractor* should ensure that he is aware of the Equipment included in each of cost component headings 2 and 4. In ECC3, accommodation is part of Equipment.

Different approaches are used for Equipment in the full SCC and the Shorter SCC. Some *Employers* find the full SCC approach to Equipment to be cumbersome and difficult to apply and therefore choose to use the Shorter SCC only; however, it could be that the *Contractor* who owns Equipment may be better or worse off in an assessment made under the Shorter SSC.[191] Some *Employers* have chosen to avoid this by using an Option Z clause to delete cost component heading 2 of the full SCC and replace it with cost component heading 2 of the Shorter SCC. The relevant items in Contract Data part two should also be deleted.

Changes from ECC2 to ECC3 are as follows:

- The cost of accommodation is now part of Equipment and **not** the Working Area Overheads percentage, as defined in 4 Charges in ECC2.
- The depreciation and maintenance charge calculations in ECC2 have been replaced with 'open market rates', rather than the theoretical surrogate hire charge calculated using the depreciation and maintenance charge.
- Payments for Equipment purchased for work included in this contract is a new component of cost.

2.8.3.1 Equipment using the full SCC

ECC2

The full SCC includes a number of components for the cost of Equipment, admissible as Actual Cost such as:

21 Hire (externally hired Equipment). ECC3 includes rented Equipment.
22 Depreciation and maintenance (non-externally hired Equipment). ECC3 depreciation and maintenance charge replaced with 'open market rates'.
23 Consumables (Equipment which is consumed, e.g. fuel). ECC3 renumbered 25.
24 Transporting, erection and dismantling, upgrading and modification. ECC3 renumbered 26.

The cost of items 21 and 23 of the above normally present no difficulty. Item 22, however, is a different matter altogether. By non-externally hired Equipment is meant either:

- Equipment bought and paid for by the *Contractor* either specifically for the contract or previously or
- Equipment purchased by the *Contractor* under a hire purchase or lease agreement or Equipment hired by the *Contractor* from the *Contractor's* parent company or another part of the group with the same parent company – that is, internally hired Equipment.

ECC3

The full SCC includes a number of components for the cost of Equipment, admissible as Defined Cost such as:

21 Hire or rental (externally hired Equipment).

---

[190]ECC2 clause 11.2(11); ECC3 clause 11.2(7).
[191]Especially if some element of the *Contractor's* compensation event quotation is delay related. As noted in B. Eggleston, *The New Engineering Contract: a commentary*, Blackwell Science, Oxford, 1996, p. 61.

22   Payments for Equipment which is not listed in the Contract Data but is
* owned by the *Contractor*,
* purchased by the *Contractor* under a hire purchase or lease agreement or
* hired by the *Contractor* from the *Contractor*'s parent company or from a company with the same parent company.
23   Payments for Equipment purchased for work included in this contract.
24   Payments for special Equipment listed in the Contract Data.
25   Consumables (Equipment which is consumed, e.g. fuel).
26   Transporting, erection and dismantling, upgrading and modification.
27   Payments for purchase of materials used to construct or fabricate Equipment.

The changes to Equipment made in ECC3 address the issues that have come up during the use of ECC2 and the new headings provide a more comprehensive and practical approach to Equipment.

The components of cost for ECC2 are discussed below.

2.8.3.1A Hire (21 in ECC2)   No Contract Data entries are required for externally hired Equipment.

Any entries in an application for payment should be supported by documentary evidence such as invoices from the hiring company and plant records or time sheets that show for what activity the item of Equipment was used and for how long.

2.8.3.1B Depreciation and maintenance (22 in ECC2)   Due to the difficulties in assessing whether the rates charged by the *Contractor* for 2.8.3.1A of Equipment are fair, the ECC uses a depreciation and maintenance charge approach which the ECC Guidance Notes state is intended to streamline the process of identifying the costs of '*Contractor*-owned' Equipment.

Depreciation and maintenance is applicable on items of Equipment that are owned by the *Contractor*, purchased by the *Contractor* under a hire purchase agreement or hired by the *Contractor* from the *Contractor*'s parent company. This cost component therefore covers all instances other than the hiring of Equipment from a third party.

The explanation in the SCC of how to apply this cost component is clear; however, there could be some choices with regard to working life and purchase price that might not be agreeable to both Parties, and this is why many *Employers* prefer to use the Shorter SCC only.

Contracts Data part two entries are required for depreciation and maintenance as follows:

Not used with the Shorter Schedule of Cost Components   • Except for special items the percentage for Equipment depreciation and maintenance is..........................%

Not used with the Shorter Schedule of Cost Components   • The percentages for depreciation and maintenance for special items of Equipment are:

Equipment	Size or capacity	%
....	....	....
....	....	....

The percentages represent the depreciation charged on the *Contractor*'s books and should include:

* repairs, modifications, major overhauls, rectification and upgrading carried out prior to the Contract Date and
* the cost of any necessary registration, duties, tests and testing of Equipment and the fees and taxes on Equipment.

An example of how it works is given in Fig. 2.3.

Fig. 2.3. **Depreciation and maintenance charge**

The percentage for Equipment depreciation and maintenance is a percentage entered by the *Contractor* in part two of the Contract Data at the time he submits his tender. The percentage would need to cover any necessary registration, duties, tests and testing of Equipment, and the fees and taxes on Equipment.

Therefore assume an example where the *Contractor* has purchased a backacter for £200,000 with a useful working life of five years. Assuming a percentage for depreciation and maintenance of 20%, the amount for depreciation and maintenance for this item of Equipment (i.e. a component of Actual Cost) per week would be calculated as follows:

$$\frac{£200,000}{260\ \text{weeks}} + 20\% = £923.08/\text{week}$$

If there is a lot of *Contractor*-owned Equipment within the Working Areas, the above calculations can absorb a lot of administrative time establishing the original purchase price and agreeing the working life of the Equipment.

For simplicity therefore, the Schedule of Cost Components treats some 'Equipment' such as tools, survey instruments, computers, laboratory equipment, cabins and workshops, as an overhead under the 'Charges' in section 4.

2.8.3.1C Consumables (23 in ECC2) No Contract Data entries are required for consumables.

Some items of Equipment may be consumed while the *Contractor* is carrying out the *works*, such as fuels, welding rods and lubricants. The purchase price of these items would be included in an application for payment with the appropriate supporting documentation, such as invoices.

2.8.3.1D Transport, erection and upgrading (24 in ECC2) No Contract Data entries are required for the transportation, erection and upgrading of Equipment.

As long as the costs for the following are not included elsewhere, such as in the hire rates or the depreciation and maintenance charge, the *Contractor* may include in an application for payment for the cost of:

- transporting Equipment to and from the Working Areas,
- erecting and dismantling Equipment,
- upgrading or modification needed for a compensation event.

2.8.3.1E Cost of operatives (25 in ECC2) The cost of operatives could appear in one of three places:

(1)   in the hire rates,
(2)   in the depreciation and maintenance change (although very unlikely),
(3)   in the cost of people (as described in cost component heading 1 of the SCC).

Clearly, the cost of operatives could appear in the hire rates **and** the depreciation and maintenance charge since the two cost components are mutually exclusive; however, the cost of operatives should not appear in those cost components **and** in the cost of people.

It should also be noted that if the cost of people is included with the Equipment then you lose the percentage uplift for the Working Area overheads, which is applied to the cost of people.

2.8.3.1F Equipment using the full SCC: ECC3 only

ECC3 reviews, redefines and recategorises the components for the cost of Equipment, admissible as Defined Cost.

The changes to Equipment made in ECC3 address the issues that have come up during the use of ECC and the new headings provide a more comprehensive and practical approach to Equipment. These are discussed below.

2.8.3.1G Hire or rent of Equipment not owned by the Contractor (21 in ECC3)

No Contract Data entries are required for externally hired or rented Equipment.

Any entries in an application for payment should be supported by documentary evidence such as invoices from the hiring or rental company, and plant records or time sheets that show for what activity the item of Equipment was used and for how long.

Payments are made at the hire or rental rate multiplied by the time for which the Equipment is required.

2.8.3.1H Payments for Equipment not listed in the Contract Data (22 in ECC3)

ECC2 dealt with this category of Equipment by using a surrogate hire charge by way of the depreciation and maintenance charge which required the insertion in the Contract Data of data to be used in the hypothetical calculation.

ECC3 has done away with this requirement and simplified it to 'open market rates, multiplied by the time for which the Equipment is required'. There are therefore no Contract Data entries required. Evidence of payment would be required, as well as the time period for which the Equipment was used.

2.8.3.1J Payments for Equipment purchased for work included in this contract (23 in ECC3)

This component of cost supersedes depreciation and maintenance in ECC2. ECC3 has done away with this requirement and simplified it to 'open market rates, multiplied by the time for which the Equipment is required'. The Contract Data is required to state a time-related charge. The purchase price of the Equipment as well as its value throughout the contract and at Completion is required to be evidenced.

The *Contractor* is required to list the Equipment in Contract Data part two.

The Equipment that is purchased for work included in the contract should be listed here. The time-related charge for the Equipment as well as the time period to which the charge relates should also be included.

- The listed items of Equipment purchased for work on this contract, with an on cost charge, are

Equipment	time-related charge	per time period
....	....	....
....	....	....

2.8.3.1K Payments for special Equipment listed in the Contract Data (24 in ECC3)

ECC3 requires the *Contractor* to identify in Contract Data part two any special Equipment that he proposes to use in the contract. He is required to provide the time period for which the Equipment is used.

The *Contractor* lists here the rates for special Equipment that he intends to use, together with the rates.

- The rates for special Equipment are

Equipment	size/capacity	rate
....	....	....
....	....	....

ECC3 sensibly makes provision for the addition of special items of Equipment to be made to this list given by the *Contractor* at the time of tender in category 24.[192] It would seem that the *Contractor* is required to make a request to the *Project Manager*.

[192]If the *Project Manager* agrees, an additional item of special Equipment may be assessed as if it had been listed in the Contract Data.

This is a sensible provision since contracts are subject to change and there may be a need for special Equipment not envisaged at the outset of the contract.

2.8.3.1L Consumables (25 in ECC3)

The requirements in ECC3 are the same as for ECC2.

No Contract Data entries are required for consumables.

Some items of Equipment may be consumed while the *Contractor* is carrying out the *works*, such as fuels, welding rods and lubricants. The purchase price of these items would be included in an application for payment with the appropriate supporting documentation, such as invoices.

2.8.3.1M Transport, erection, dismantling, constructing, fabricating or modifying Equipment (26 in ECC3)

Essentially the same as ECC2 with some refinement in the wording.

No Contract Data entries are required for the transportation, erection and upgrading of Equipment.

As long as the costs for the following are not included elsewhere, such as in the hire or rental rates, the *Contractor* may include in an application for payment for the cost of:

- transporting Equipment to and from the Working Areas other than for repair or maintenance,
- erecting and dismantling Equipment and
- constructing, fabricating or modifying as a result of a compensation event.

2.8.3.1N Payments for purchase of materials used to construct or fabricate Equipment (27 in ECC3)

A new category introduced in ECC3 to cover the purchase of materials used to construct or fabricate Equipment.

2.8.3.1P Cost of operatives (28 in ECC3)

Unless included in the hire rates, the cost of operatives is included in the cost of people.

Clearly, the cost of operatives should not appear in the hire rates **and** the cost of people, as these two cost components are mutually exclusive.

You should also note that if the cost of people is included with the Equipment then you lose the percentage uplift for the Working Area overheads, which is applied to the cost of people.

2.8.3.2 Equipment using the Shorter SCC: ECC2 only

The Shorter SCC includes a number of components for the cost of Equipment, such as:

21 Equipment included in a published list (such as the Civil Engineering Contractors Association (CECA) Daywork Schedule),
22 Equipment not included in a published list,
23 idle and standby time,
24 transporting, erection and dismantling, upgrading and modification,
25 consumables,
26 cost of operatives.

2.8.3.2A Equipment in a published list (21 in ECC2 SSCC)

Rather than using historical data about Equipment, such as its working life and purchase price, the Shorter SCC relies on a published list of Equipment with accompanying rates. The published list envisaged here would generally be a nationally published list such as the CECA Daywork Schedule. It may be that the *Contractor* has an internally published list of owned Equipment that is used for other non-ECC jobs and that he wishes to have incorporated into the ECC as the published list. It is possible that such a list may be acceptable to the *Employer* subject to audit of the rates included in the list.

Contract Data entries are required for items included in a published list of Equipment.

- The published list of Equipment is the last edition of the list published by ....

- The percentage for adjustment for listed Equipment is .... %

The percentage adjustment to the published rates is required for the following reasons. The rates in the CECA Daywork Schedule, for example, include an element for overhead and profit. Since in the ECC these are always included in the Fee, the CECA Daywork Schedule rates should be adjusted downwards so that profits and overheads are not claimed twice by the *Contractor*. In addition, in some cases the published rates might not be appropriate to local circumstances and might need further adjustments upwards or downwards.

In some instances, one percentage may not be reasonable to use as a blanket adjustment for all items of Equipment, and the *Contractor* should then apply different percentages as required.

2.8.3.2B Equipment not in a published list (22 in ECC2 SSCC)

Contract Data entries are required for items **not** included in a published list of Equipment, if they are likely to be a considerable cost and are not included in the published list in cost component 21. These could include items such as scaffolding and temporary sheet piling.

- The rates of other Equipment are

Equipment	size or capacity	rate
....	....	....
....	....	....

The rate as well as a description of the Equipment should be stated.

2.8.3.2C Idle and standby time (23 in ECC2 SSCC)

It is not clear whether idle and standby time as described in the Shorter SCC are obligatory or not. It is suggested that *Project Managers* are circumspect when applying this cost component.

For idle and standby time, deductions are made on the following basis:

- the first two hours for items paid at an hourly rate,
- the first half day for items paid at a daily rate,
- the first third of a week for items paid at a weekly rate and
- the first quarter of a month for items paid at a monthly rate.

2.8.3.2D Transporting, erection and dismantling, upgrading and modification (24 in ECC2 SSCC)

No Contract Data entries are required for the transportation, erection and upgrading of Equipment.

As long as the costs for the following are not included elsewhere, such as in the hire rates or the depreciation and maintenance charge, the *Contractor* may include in an application for payment for the cost of:

- transporting Equipment to and from the Working Areas,
- erecting and dismantling Equipment,
- upgrading or modification needed for a compensation event.

2.8.3.2E Consumables (25 in ECC2 SSCC)

No Contract Data entries are required for consumables.

Some items of Equipment may be consumed while the *Contractor* is carrying out the *works*, such as fuels, welding rods and lubricants. The purchase price of these items would be included in an application for payment with the appropriate supporting documentation, such as invoices, included as well.

2.8.3.2F Other components of cost (in ECC2 SSCC)

Note that the Shorter SCC does not distinguish between Equipment that is hired and Equipment that is *Contractor*-owned, and so all such Equipment will be paid for in accordance with the published list. It is suggested that a more equitable arrangement would be for hired Equipment to be paid on invoice as it is in the full SCC, and that *Contractor*-owned Equipment only is paid in accordance with the rates in the published list. An Option Z clause could be drafted to introduce this cost component into the Shorter SCC.

Documentary evidence, such as invoices, is sufficient for the other categories. See explanations above for the remainder of the cost components in the Shorter SCC.

2.8.3.2G Equipment using the Shorter SCC: ECC3 ONLY

The Shorter SCC in ECC3 is very similar to that in ECC2. There are however a number of changes which are highlighted below. The Shorter SCC components in ECC3 for the cost of Equipment is as follows:

21 Equipment included in a published list (such as the Civil Engineering Contractors Association (CECA) Daywork Schedule). In ECC3 Equipment includes the cost of the *Contractor*'s accommodation. It was felt by many that the inclusion of the *Contractor*'s on-site accommodation by way of an allowance in the people percentage was not practical. Indeed many users in ECC2 have amended their contracts so that the *Contractor*'s accommodation would be treated in the same way as for Equipment.
22 Equipment not included in a published list.
23 The time required. The provision for idle and standby time has been deleted in ECC3.
24 Transporting, erection and dismantling, upgrading and modification.
25 Consumables.
26 Cost of operatives.
27 Equipment which is neither in the published list stated in the Contract Data nor listed in the Contract Data.

2.8.3.2H Equipment in a published list (21 in ECC3 SSCC)

This component is the same as ECC2. Contract Data entries are required for items included in a published list of Equipment.

Data for the Shorter Schedule of Cost Components

- The published list of Equipment is the last edition of the list published by ....

Data for the Shorter Schedule of Cost Components

The percentage for adjustment for Equipment in published list is .... % (state plus or minus)

2.8.3.2J Equipment not in a published list (22 in ECC3 SSCC)

This component is the same as ECC2. Contract Data entries are required for items **not** included in a published list of Equipment.

Data for the Shorter Schedule of Cost Components

- The rates of other Equipment are

Equipment	size or capacity	rate
....	....	....
....	....	....

The rate as well as a description of the Equipment should be stated.

2.8.3.2K The time required (23 in ECC3 SSCC)

This clause now gives a statement outlining how the time required for an item of Equipment is to be expressed.

'23 The time required is expressed in hours, days, weeks or months consistently with the list of items of Equipment stated in the Contract Data or with the published list stated in the Contract Data.'

2.8.3.2L Transporting, erection and dismantling, constructing, fabricating or modifying Equipment (24 in ECC3 SSCC)

No Contract Data entries are required for the transportation, erection and upgrading of Equipment.

As long as the costs for the following are not included elsewhere, such as in the hire rates or the depreciation and maintenance charge, the *Contractor* may include in an application for payment for the cost of:

- transporting Equipment to and from the Working Areas other than for repair and maintenance,
- erecting and dismantling Equipment, and

- constructing, fabricating or modifying Equipment as a result of a compensation event.

2.8.3.2M Consumables (25 in ECC3 SSCC)

No Contract Data entries are required for consumables.

This is treated the same as in ECC2.

2.8.3.2N Cost of Operatives (26 in ECC3 SSCC)

The same as ECC2. Unless included in the hire rates, the cost of operatives is included in the cost of people.

Clearly, the cost of operatives should not appear in the hire rates **and** the cost of people, as these two cost components are mutually exclusive.

You should also note that if the cost of people is included with the Equipment then you lose the percentage uplift for the Working Area overheads, which is applied to the cost of people.

2.8.3.2P Equipment not on a published list or listed in the Contract Data (27 in ECC3 SSCC)

Where Equipment is neither in a published list stated in the Contract Data nor listed in the Contract Data, then this Equipment is assessed 'at competitively tendered or open market rates'. The onus will be on the *Contractor* to demonstrate that the rates put forward fulfil this criteria.

2.8.4 Cost component heading 3: Plant and Materials

Plant and Materials are items that are intended to be included in the *works*,[193] for example boilers, turbines, steelwork, pumps, vessels, agitators, cabling, cable trays, concrete, structural steel.

The items of Plant and Materials included in the *Contractors* Actual/Defined Cost would not include items issued to the *Contractor* by the *Employer* free of charge.

The cost components for Plant and Materials as described in both the full and the Shorter SCC comprise:

- purchasing Plant and Materials,
- delivery to and removal from Working Areas,
- providing and removing packaging,
- samples and tests.

There are no entries for Plant and Materials required for Contract Data part two since any application for payment would include invoices and other proof of payment. Note that there are aspects of Disallowed Cost that pertain to Plant and Materials (i.e. there are some items of cost for which the *Contractor* does not get paid).

Since most of Plant and Materials tend to be supplied by third parties outsourced by the *Contractor* and consequently the subject of supply contracts, the Actual Cost[194] of Plant and Materials is relatively easy to identify by reference to the invoices received. Clause 52.1 of the contract makes it clear that all amounts included in Actual Cost[195] are to have 'all discounts, rebates and taxes, which can be recovered, deducted'. Disallowed Cost as defined includes the 'cost of Plant and Materials not used to Provide the Works', so it will be necessary to identify any over-ordering by the *Contractor* and to adjust the Actual Cost[196] accordingly.

Item 32 makes it clear that cost is credited with payments received for disposal of Plant and Materials (ECC3: unless the cost is disallowed).

2.8.5 Cost component heading 4: Charges

Charges include some items of Equipment, such as site huts and welfare facilities, security and hand-held tools. In ECC3 the cost of the *Contractor*'s accommodation is now included under Equipment.

---

[193]ECC2 clause 11.2(10); ECC3 clause 11.2(12).
[194]ECC3 Defined Cost.
[195]ECC3 Defined Cost.
[196]ECC3 Defined Cost.

This cost category covers a range of cost components, which collectively could be loosely described as site overheads[197] (excluding people) or indirect costs. Some of the cost components (generally those that are unique to the particular contract) are directly reimbursable (items 41, 42 and 43 of the full Schedule of Cost Components) and others, the majority of which are common to all contracts, are covered by a percentage tendered by the *Contractor* – the Working Area overhead percentage for the full SCC – applied to the Actual Cost[198] of people items 11, 12 and 13 of the full Schedule of Cost Components.

Different approaches are used in the full SCC and the Shorter SCC.

2.8.5.1 Charges using the full SCC for both ECC2 and ECC3

2.8.5.1A Cost components (41, 42 and 43)

The full SCC allows for the direct cost for some aspects of charges, such as water, gas and electricity, as well as rent of premises in the Working Areas and financing charges. These cost components described within items 41, 42 and 43 of the full SCC would, for the most part, be supportable by documentary evidence and therefore there are no Contract Data part two entries required for these cost components.

It is worth discussing the financing charges mentioned in ECC2 item 43(a) of the FSCC in a little more detail. Payment in the ECC works in arrears, as it does with most contracts. In other words, the *Contractor* submits an application for payment at the end of March for work done during the month of March. He gets paid for this work around the end of April and has therefore had to finance the work for a month or more (in the case of invoices paid during March). Some *Contractors* have included in their application for payment[199] a cost for this financing as a finance charge under item 43 of the full SCC. There is a way for *Employers* to prevent this happening, and that would be to pay accrued costs rather than paid costs. This would involve using secondary Option Z to amend some of the payment clauses and it would also involve more intense audits to ensure that accrued costs have actually been paid later by the *Contractor* to balance his books. This concept is also discussed in Chapter 2 of Book 2 on contract options.

2.8.5.1B Overhead costs (44)

Also allowed under the full SCC is a charge for the overhead costs incurred within the Working Areas (also known as site establishment), calculated by applying the percentage for Working Areas Overheads stated in Contract Data part two to the total of People items 11, 12 and 13 (and 14 in ECC3). These overhead costs as represented by the percentage include[200] items such as:

- site huts,[201]
- catering,[202]
- sanitation,
- security,
- computing,
- hand tools and hand-held power tools,

and would generally be called site establishment.

Clearly, the more or fewer people that are on Site results in greater or smaller people costs, amending the total after applying the percentage, and this poses a problem. At tender stage, the *Contractor* can make an estimate of the costs based on his projected programme and the number of people he intends to man the job. If numerous compensation events occur, which may be inevitable in Options C, D and particularly E, these projected histograms could become increasingly incorrect and the *Contractor* may get over- or under-compensated for his costs. The answer to this problem is not an easy one. If both *Project Managers* and *Contractors* are aware of the problem, however, perhaps some compromise may be sought as the project progresses.

[197]Note that some costs that are traditionally known as site overheads, such as the site agent, would tend to be included in the cost of people (cost component heading 1).
[198]ECC3 Defined Cost.
[199]For Options C, D and E.
[200]Please note that this is not a complete list. See the ECC2 page 51 under 44 for a complete list.
[201]ECC3 included in Equipment.
[202]ECC3 for items such as catering you will need to differentiate between the accommodation and the provision and use of Equipment, supplies and services.

The Contract Data part two entry for this site establishment cost is as follows. Note that this could be called preliminaries, except that supervision on the site would generally be under the cost component for people.

Not used with the Shorter Schedule of Cost Components
- The percentage for Working Areas overheads is .... %

In ECC3 the Contract Data is as follows:

Data for Schedule of Cost Components
- The percentage for Working Areas overheads is .... %

2.8.5.2 Charges using the Shorter SCC in ECC2

The Shorter SCC caters for all of the items listed under the full SCC as a percentage for people overheads,[203] which is included in Contract Data part two. All items, including gas, electricity, payments to public authorities, payments for financing charges, as well as site huts,[204] sanitation and so on, are therefore included in the percentage for people overheads. Consequently, this percentage is likely to be greater than the Working Area overhead percentage used in the full SCC.

To arrive at the charge, the percentage is multiplied by the total of People items 11, 12 and 13.

The Contract Data part two entry required for the Shorter SCC is as follows:

Only used with the Shorter Schedule of Cost Components
- The percentage for **people** overheads is .... %

Note that the same problems regarding People costs apply here.

2.8.5.3 Charges using the Shorter SCC in ECC3

The Shorter SCC caters for all of the items listed under the full SCC as a percentage for people overheads,[205] which is included in Contract Data part two. There are five components of cost, not four as in the FSCC. All items, including gas, electricity, payments to public authorities, payments for cancellation charges.[206] Sanitation and so on, are therefore included in the percentage for People overheads.

ECC3: the Contract Data part two entry required is as follows:

Data for the Shorter Schedule of Cost Components
- The percentage for people overheads is .... %

2.8.6 Cost component heading 5: Manufacture and fabrication outside the Working Areas

The cost components for manufacture and fabrication outside the Working Areas include the cost of manufacture or fabrication of Plant and Materials that are:

- wholly or partly designed specifically for the *works* and
- manufactured or fabricated outside the Working Areas.

This cost component excludes the costs of manufacture or fabrication of Plant and Materials that are 'off the shelf'.[207]

The information required from the *Contractor* in Contract Data part two is the same for both the full and the Shorter SCC (except for the SSCC in ECC3).

The *Contractor* tenders in Contract Data part two an hourly rate for the categories of his own employees who would work in a workshop or factory outside the Working Areas. He also tenders a percentage for manufacturing

---

[203]Rather than some cost components being supported by documentary evidence as in the full SCC, all cost components are included in one percentage.
[204]ECC3 accommodation is included in Equipment.
[205]Rather than some cost components being supported by documentary evidence as in the full SCC, all cost components are included in one percentage.
[206]ECC3 accommodation is included in Equipment.
[207]Which would appear under cost components heading 3 of the SCC.

---

and fabrication overheads that takes into account the overheads applicable to manufacture and fabrication only. (See Fig. 2.2 and Table 2.3.)

ECC2 only
- The hourly rates for Actual Cost of manufacture or fabrication outside the Working Areas are

Category of employee   Hourly rate

....

....

....

- The percentage for manufacture or fabrication overheads is .... %.

ECC3 only
- The hourly rates for Defined Cost of manufacture or fabrication outside the Working Areas are

category of employee   hourly rate

....

....

....

- The percentage for manufacture or fabrication overheads is .... %.

The percentage would include for equipment, machinery and tools used in fabrication shops outside the Working Areas and may be several hundred per cent of the labour costs.

Note that these overheads are separate from the overheads included in the *fee percentage* and therefore both sets of overheads are used in the calculation of the Price for Work Done to Date. Consequently, the *fee percentage* should not include for the overheads included in the percentage for manufacture or fabrication overheads. Note also that the rates for employees should not include profit or overheads since this amount is included in the *fee percentage* and in the overhead percentage respectively.

The ECC Guidance Notes state that the use of cost-reimbursable contracts is not recommended where manufacture or fabrication outside the Working Areas forms a major part of a contract because of the difficulty this presents in the control and identification of Actual Cost.[208] The same could be said to apply where design outside the Working Areas forms a major part of a contract. For this reason the ECC takes a very cautious approach, relying on the tendered hourly rates and overhead percentages inserted by the *Contractor* in Contract Data part two as the basis for calculating the Actual Cost of these activities. It only requires therefore for the *Project Manager* to satisfy himself as to the time spent by the *Contractor* on these activities.

A possible solution in this situation would be to consider having an Option A fixed-price contract for the manufacture and supply of, say, the pipework. However, this would still not remove the problems associated if compensation events arise.

In ECC3, there are no Contract Data entries required in the SSCC, since the amounts are paid by the *Contractor*.

2.8.7 Cost component heading 6: Design outside the Working Areas

The cost components for Design outside the Working Areas comprise design of the *works* and Equipment done outside the Working Areas.

The information required from the *Contractor* in Contract Data part two is the same for both the full and the Shorter SCC.

The *Contractor* would tender in his Contract Data part two the categories of employees his own who would work on design, as well as the categories of employees who would travel to and from the Working Areas for the purposes of design, and any overheads involved in the design outside the Working Areas.

[208]ECC3 Defined Cost.

ECC2

- The hourly rates for Actual Cost of design outside the Working Areas are

Category of employee   Hourly rate

....

....

....

- The percentage for design overheads is .... %
- The categories of employees whose travelling expenses to and from the Working Areas are included in Actual Cost are:

....

....

ECC3

- The hourly rates for Defined Cost of design outside the Working Areas are

category of employee   hourly rate

....

....

....

- The percentage for design overheads is .... %
- The categories of design employees whose travelling expenses to and from the Working Areas are included in Defined Cost on:

....

....

The percentage would include for the cost of computer facilities and reprographic facilities for design outside the Working Areas.

Note that these overheads are separate from the overheads included in the *fee percentage* (ECC3 *direct fee percentage*) and therefore both sets of overheads are used in the calculation of the Price for Work Done to Date. Consequently, the *fee percentage* (ECC3 *direct fee percentage*) should not include for the overheads included in the percentage for design overheads. Note also that the rates for employees should not include profit or overheads since this amount is included in the *fee percentage* (ECC3 *direct fee percentage*) and in the overhead percentage respectively. See Fig. 2.3.

2.8.8 Cost component heading 7: Insurance

Item 7 of the Schedule of Cost Components provides for the following to be deducted from Actual/Defined Cost:

- the cost of events for which this contract requires the *Contractor* to insure and
- other costs paid to the *Contractor* by insurers.

The first avoids the *Employer* having to pay for costs that the *Contractor* should have insured against. If the *Contractor* does not insure as required by the contract then such costs are at his own risk. An example of the first category is loss of or damage to Equipment, which clause 84.1 requires the *Contractor* to insure against. If a piece of Equipment owned and being used by the *Contractor* to Provide the Works catches fire and is destroyed, then its replacement cost is deducted from Actual/Defined Cost. This avoids the *Employer* having to pay for costs which the *Contractor* should have insured against. If the *Contractor* does not insure as required by the contract then such costs are at his own risk. In practice such an eventuality should never arise if the *Project Manager* requests evidence from the *Contractor* that the required insurances are in force (refer to clause 85.1).

The second deduction ensures that the *Contractor* does not receive double payment as a result, for example, of insurance, which he has voluntarily taken out or from insuring for a greater cover than required by the contract. The practical complication with this is that unless the *Contractor* volunteers the information, the *Employer* will not know the scope of any difference in cover (DIC) insurance the *Contractor* has effected.

There are no Contract Data entries required for this cost component heading.

2.9 Contract Data part two

Note that the data for the Schedule of Cost Components shown in the individual component headings above do not appear in the same order in Contract Data part two. Contract Data part two lists the off-site components first and then follows with the on-site components for the full SCC and then the Shorter SCC.

2.10 Putting it all together for payment – Options C, D and E, ECC2 only

Once the cost of the each of the component headings can be ascertained, it is a matter of adding up the costs for each heading. A suggested format follows (Table 2.4); however, each *Contractor* may use the calculation that most suits him. ECC2 appears first, then the ECC3.

Table 2.4. Pulling the SCC together – ECC2 only

1	People		£ total
11 12 13	Components for 11, 12 and 13 • For people directly employed by the *Contractor* and whose normal place of working is within the Working Areas	Payroll sheets for the period concerned	£
11 12 13	Components for 11, 12 and 13 • For people directly employed by the *Contractor* and whose normal place of working is **not** within the Working Areas, but who are working within the Working Areas for a period of not less than one week	Payroll sheets for the period concerned	£
11 12 13	Components for 11, 12 and 13 • For people who are **not** directly employed by the *Contractor*, but are paid by the *Contractor* according to the time worked while they are within the Working Areas	Payroll sheets for the period concerned	£

2a	Equipment for the full SCC		
	Note: This Equipment does not include the Equipment included in component heading 4 Charges, for example site offices and workshops, welfare.		
21	Payments for the hire of Equipment not owned by the *Contractor*, the *Contractor*'s parent company or by another part of a group within the same parent company	Invoices and proof of payment	£
22	Depreciation and maintenance of Equipment owned by the *Contractor*, purchased by him under lease or hire purchase agreement or hired from the parent company or another part of the group within the same company	Actual purchase price of the Equipment divided by its average working life, multiplied by the time and increasing the product by the percentage included in Contract Data part two	£
23	Purchase price of Equipment that is consumed, for example fuel, lubricants, shuttering materials, welding rods	Invoice and proof of payment	£
24	Transporting Equipment to and from Working Areas (unless in 22)	Invoice and proof of payment	£
24	Erecting and dismantling Equipment (unless in 22)	Documentary proof of payment	£
24	Upgrading or modification needed for a compensation event (unless in 22)	Documentary proof of payment	£
25	Cost of operatives is always included either in 21/22 or in 1	Not calculated	0

2b	Equipment for the Shorter SCC (alternative to the full SCC)		
21	Amounts in the published list stated in Contract Data part two	Rates in the published list multiplied by the percentage adjustment in Contract Data part two, multiplied by the time for which the Equipment is required	£
22	Amounts **not** in the published list stated in Contract Data part two	Rates in Contract Data part two multiplied by the time for which the Equipment is required	£

23	Idle and standby time	• The first two hours for items paid at an hourly rate	£
		• The first half day for items paid at a daily rate	£
		• The first third of a week for items paid at a weekly rate	£
		• The first quarter of a month for items paid at a monthly rate	£
24	Transporting Equipment to and from Working Areas (unless in 21)	Invoice and proof of payment	£
24	Erecting and dismantling Equipment (unless in 21)	Documentary proof of payment	£
24	Upgrading or modification needed for a compensation event (unless in 21)	Documentary proof of payment	£
25	Purchase price of Equipment that is consumed (unless in 21)	Invoice and proof of payment	£
26	Cost of operatives is always included either in 21 or in 1	Not calculated	0

3   Plant and Materials

31a	Payments for purchasing Plant and Materials	Invoice and proof of payment	£
31b	Payments for delivery to and from the Working Areas	Invoice and proof of payment	£
31c	Payments for providing and removing packaging	Documentary proof of payment	£
31d	Payments for samples and tests	Documentary proof of payment	£
32	Payments received for the disposal of Plant and Materials	Documentary proof of payment	−£

4a   Charges for the full SCC

41	Payments to utilities for provision and use in the Working Areas of (a) water (b) gas (c) electricity (d) other services	Invoice and proof of payment	£ £ £ £
42	Payments to public authorities, utilities for charges they are authorised to make in respect of the *works*	Invoice and proof of payment	£
43	Payments for (a) financing charges (b) buying or leasing land (c) compensation for loss of crops or building (d) royalties (e) inspection certificates (f) rent of premises in the Working Areas (g) charges for access to the Working Areas (h) facilities for visits to the Working Areas by Others (i) specialist services	Invoice or other document and proof of payment	£ £ £ £ £ £ £ £
44	A charge for overhead costs in the Working Areas	Percentage for Working Areas overheads in Contract Data part two, multiplied by the total of people items 11, 12 and 13	£

4b   Charges for the Shorter SCC (alternative to the full SCC)

| | A charge for costs in the Working Areas | Percentage for **People** overheads in Contract Data part two, multiplied by the cost for people items 11, 12 and 13 | £ |

5   Manufacture and fabrication outside the Working Areas

| 51
52 | Cost of manufacture or fabrication of Plant and Materials which are wholly or specifically designed for the *works*, and which are manufactured or fabricated outside the Working Areas | (Hourly rates in Contract Data part two multiplied by hours worked) added to (that product multiplied by the percentage for manufacturing and fabrication overheads in Contract Data part two) | £ |

6	Design outside the Working Areas			
61 62	Cost of design of the *works* and Equipment done outside the Working Areas	(Hourly rates in Contract Data part two multiplied by hours worked) added to (that product multiplied by the percentage for design overheads in Contract Data part two)		£
63	Cost of travel to and from the Working Areas for the categories of employees listed in Contract Data part two	Invoice/tickets or business mileage plus proof of payment		

7	Insurance			
	The cost of events for which the contract requires the *Contractor* to insure	Documentary proof of payment		−£
	Other costs paid to the *Contractor* by insurers	Documentary proof of payment		−£
			Total of the SCC	£

2.11 Putting it all together for payment – Options C, D and E, ECC3 only

Once the cost of the each of the component headings can be ascertained, it is a matter of adding up the costs for each heading. A suggested format follows (Table 2.5); however, each *Contractor* may use the calculation that most suits him.

Table 2.5. Pulling the SCC together – ECC3 only

1	People		£ total
11 12 13	Components for 11, 12 and 13 • People directly employed by the *Contractor* and whose normal place of working is within the Working Areas	Payroll sheets for the period concerned	£
11 12 13	Components for 11, 12 and 13 • People who are directly employed by the *Contractor* and whose normal place of working is not within the Working Areas but who are working within the Working Areas	Payroll sheets for the period concerned	£
14	The following components of the cost of people who are not directly employed by the *Contractor*, but are paid by the *Contractor* according to the time worked while they are within the Working Areas Amounts paid by the *Contractor*	Proof of payment of amounts made	£

2a	Equipment for the full SCC		
	Note: In ECC3 the definition of Equipment includes accommodation, but excludes Equipment costs covered by the percentage for Working Area overheads		
21	Payments for the hire of Equipment not owned by the *Contractor*, the *Contractor*'s parent company or by another part of a group within the same parent company	Invoices and proof of payment – hire rate or rental rate multiplied by the time for which the Equipment is required	£
22	Payments for Equipment which is not listed in the Contract Data, but is • owned by the *Contractor* • purchased by the *Contractor* under a hire purchase or lease agreement • hired by the *Contractor* from the *Contractor*'s parent company or from a company with the same parent company	Invoices and proof of payment – at open market rates multiplied by the time for which the Equipment is required	£
23	Payments for Equipment purchased for work included in this contract listed with a time-related on-cost charge, in the Contract Data, of • the change in value over the period for which the Equipment is required and • the time-related on-cost charge stated in the Contract Data for the period for which the Equipment is required	• Proof of purchase • Time-related on-cost from Contract Data • Demonstration of the change in value over period	£

24	Payments for special Equipment listed in the Contract Data	Rates in Contract Data multiplied by the time for which the Equipment is required		
25	Payments for purchase price of Equipment which is consumed	Invoice and proof of payment		£
26	Unless included in the hire or rental rates, payments for • transporting Equipment to and from the Working Areas other than for repair and maintenance • erecting and dismantling Equipment • constructing, fabricating or modifying Equipment as a result of a compensation event	Documentary proof of payment		£
27	Payments for purchase of materials used to construct or fabricate Equipment	Documentary proof of payment		£
28	Unless included in the hire rates, the cost of operatives is included in the cost of people	Not calculated		0

2b Equipment for the Shorter SCC (alternative to the full SCC)

21	Amounts in the published list stated in Contract Data part two	Rates in the published list multiplied by the percentage adjustment in Contract Data part two, multiplied by the time for which the Equipment is required		£
22	Amounts **not** in the published list stated in Contract Data part two	Rates in Contract Data part two multiplied by the time for which the Equipment is required		£
23	The time required is expressed in hours, days, weeks or months consistent with the list of items of Equipment in the Contract Data or with the published list stated in the Contract Data	Statement of how to calculate time for the Equipment		0
24	Unless included in the published list, payments for • transporting Equipment to and from the Working Areas other than for repair and maintenance • erecting and dismantling Equipment • constructing, fabricating or modifying Equipment as a result of a compensation event	Invoice and proof of payment		£
25	Purchase price of Equipment that is consumed. Unless in the published list or the rate includes the purchase price	Documentary proof of payment		£
26	Cost of operatives is always included either in cost component 1 or 21 or 22	Statement of where to include people costs		0
27	Amounts for Equipment which is neither in the published list stated in the Contract Data nor listed in the Contract Data, at competitively tendered or open market rates, multiplied by the time for which the Equipment is required	Invoice and proof of payment		£

3 Plant and Materials

31	Payments for • purchasing Plant and Materials • delivery to and from the Working Areas • providing and removing packaging • samples and tests	Invoice and documentary proof of payment		£
32	Payments received for the disposal of Plant and Materials	Documentary proof of payment		−£

4a Charges for the full SCC

41	Payments for provision and use in the Working Areas of • water • gas • electricity	Invoice and proof of payment		£ £ £

42	Payments to public authorities and other properly constituted authorities which they are authorised to make payment in respect of the *works*	Invoice and proof of payment		£
43	Payments for (a) cancellation charges arising from a compensation event (b) buying or leasing land (c) compensation for loss of crops or building (d) royalties (e) inspection certificates (f) charges for access to the Working Areas (g) facilities for visits to the Working Areas by Others (h) specialist services (i) consumables and equipment provided by the Contractor for the *Project Manager*'s and *Supervisor*'s offices	Invoice or other document and proof of payment		£ £ £ £ £ £ £ £ £
44	A charge for overhead costs in the Working Areas. The charge includes provision and use of equipment, supplies and services, but excludes accommodation for (a) catering (b) medical facilities and first aid (c) recreation (d) sanitation (e) security (f) copying (g) telephone, telex, fax, radio and CCTV (h) surveying and setting out (i) computing (j) hand tools not powered by compressed air	Percentage for Working Areas overheads in Contract Data part two, multiplied by the total of people items 11, 12, 13 and 14		£

4b Charges for the Shorter SCC (alternative to the full SCC)

41	A charge for costs in the Working Areas Percentage for people overheads in Contract Data part two multiplied by the cost for people items 11 to cover costs of • payments for the provision and use in the Working Areas of water, gas and electricity • payments for buying or leasing land, compensation for loss of crops or buildings, royalties, inspection certificates, charges for access to the Working Areas, facilities for visits to the Working Areas by Others and • payments for equipment, supplies and services for offices, drawing office, laboratories, workshops, stores and compounds, labour camps, cabins, catering, medical facilities and first aid, recreation, sanitation, security, copying, telephone, telex, fax, radio, CCTV, surveying and setting out, computing, and hand tools not powered by compressed air	Percentage for people overheads in Contract Data part two multiplied by the cost for people items 11		
42	Payments for cancellation charges arising from a compensation event	Documentary proof		£
43	Payments to public authorities and other properly constituted authorities of charges which they are authorised to make in respect of *works*	Documentary proof		£
44	Consumables and equipment provided by the Contractor for the *Project Manager*'s and *Supervisor*'s office	Documentary proof		£
45	Specialist services	Documentary proof		£

5a **Manufacture and fabrication outside the Working Areas for FSCC**

51 52	Cost of manufacture or fabrication of Plant and Materials which are wholly or specifically designed for the *works* and which are manufactured or fabricated outside the Working Areas	(Hourly rates in Contract Data part two multiplied by hours worked) added to (that product multiplied by the percentage for manufacturing and fabrication overheads in Contract Data part two)		£

5b **Manufacture and fabrication outside the Working Areas for SSCC (alternative to the full SCC)**

51	Amounts paid by the *Contractor*	Documentary proof		£

6 **Design outside the Working Areas**

61 62	Cost of design of the *works* and Equipment done outside the Working Areas	(Hourly rates in Contract Data part two multiplied by hours worked) added to (that product multiplied by the percentage for design overheads in Contract Data part two)		£
63	Cost of travel to and from the Working Areas for the categories of employees listed in Contract Data part two	Invoice/tickets or business mileage plus proof of payment		

7 **Insurance**

	The cost of events for which the contract requires the *Contractor* to insure	Documentary proof of payment		−£
	Other costs paid to the *Contractor* by insurers	Documentary proof of payment		−£

		Total of the SCC	£

The final calculation for presentation in an application for the amount due for payment in ECC2 is shown in Table 2.6.

Table 2.6. Presentation in the application for payment – ECC2

1	Total of the cost components in the SCC	£
2	**Plus** payments due to Subcontractors	£
3	**Less** Disallowed Cost	−£
4	Total Actual Cost	£
5	*fee percentage* %	
6	**Add** total Actual Cost multiplied by *fee percentage*	£
7	Price for Work Done to Date (PWDD)	£
8	**Other amounts**	
9	**plus** other amounts to be paid to the *Contractor* (interest on late payments, etc.)	+£
10	**less** other amounts to be paid or retained from the *Contractor*, e.g. retention and other amounts	−£
11	**less** previous amounts due for payment	−£
12	**Total Amount due for this application**	£

The final calculation for presentation in an application for the amount due for payment in ECC3 is shown in Table 2.7.

Table 2.7. Presentation in the application for payment – ECC3

	Direct work	
1	Total of the cost components in the SCC	£
2	Less Disallowed Cost	−£
3	Total direct Defined Cost	£
4	*direct fee percentage* %	
5	**Add** total direct Defined Cost multiplied by the *direct fee percentage*	%
6	total direct work =	£
	Subcontracted work	
7	Total of the cost components in the SCC	£
8	Less Disallowed Cost	−£
9	Total subcontracted Defined Cost	£
10	*subcontracted fee percentage* %	
11	**Add** total subcontracted Defined Cost multiplied by the *subcontracted fee percentage*	%
12	total subcontracted work =	£
13	Price for Work Done to Date (PWDD) Total of items 6 and 12	£
14	**Other amounts**	
15	**plus** other amounts to be paid to the *Contractor* (interest on late payments, etc.)	+£
16	**less** other amounts to be paid or retained from the *Contractor*, e.g. retention and other amounts	−£
17	**less** previous amounts due for payment	−£
18	**Total Amount due for this application**	**£**

2.12 Audits

2.12.1 Compensation events

Because the SCC is focused on the pre-assessment of change maybe many months ahead of the actual work being undertaken, then a quotation for a compensation event may not always include supporting documentation such as quotations/invoices for Plant and Materials or wage slips.

If your project is required to be audited, either by an internal or external body, then you should ensure that the departments/bodies involved realise this at the very outset of the project. It is also suggested that you consult with them at the earliest moment so that any requirements or implications that may affect the way you operate the contract can be considered and where appropriate included in the Works Information.

2.12.2 Options C, D and E

It may not be possible for the *Project Manager* to examine fully all the information in a *Contractor*'s application for payment within the one week required to issue a payment certificate. The *Project Manager* may only have sufficient time to perform a spot check of the supporting documentation and would have to rely on later audits of the *Contractor*'s books to check the Price for work Done to Date and possibly the final total of the prices.

It is recommended that the contract requires the *Contractor* to set out his application for payment in a certain way to assist the *Project Manager* in his assessment of the amount due. Although the application for payment[209] is not mandatory, *Employers* using Options C, D and particularly E might wish to insist that the *Project Manager* receives an application for payment.[210] Assessment

[209]Clause 50.4.
[210]Through the Works Information or an Option Z clause.

of the amount due would be virtually impossible if the *Contractor* does not provide all the information in an amount due prior to the assessment date. It would be to the *Contractor*'s benefit as well to ensure that all his costs were visible and easily traceable through the supporting documentation so that disputes over valuations are kept to a minimum.

For example, in the SCC People cost component (heading 1), where the *Contractor* lists his on-site labour, including supervision, he could list the people by name and job description, the job performed and the hours spent on that job. This would generally be a copy of the daily labour record into a more legible and visible format. This would be particularly important where Disallowed Costs are incurred, such as the correction of Defects, so that the *Project Manager* is able to see where the *Contractor* has deducted the time spent on the elements making up Disallowed Costs. This also underlines the importance of having the *Project Manager* on Site, in order to be aware of the performance on Site. There is, of course, an element of mutual trust and cooperation running through the contract, particularly for the application for payment, although the *Project Manager* has the ability to correct payment certificates later.[211]

Audits can pick up small things that the *Project Manager* might miss during his assessment and it could also pick up irregularities that are not noticeable in each individual application for payment but are manifest over a period of time. At the very least, an audit could reveal whether invoices claimed for under the contract have actually been paid later on. It is recommended that at least one audit is conducted for Options C, D and E contracts, and many more for longer projects.

An example of an audit plan is included in NEC Book 2 – Managing Reality: Procuring an Engineering and Construction Contract, Appendix 3.

2.13 The Shorter Schedule of Cost Components

The Shorter Schedule of Cost Components was designed to be administratively simpler and to be used for the smaller type of compensation events by agreement.[212]

In theory the value of a compensation event should be the same whether it is assessed using the full Schedule of Cost Components or the Shorter Schedule of Cost Components.

A comparison between the full and Shorter Schedule of Cost Components is given in Fig. 2.4 and a comparison between the full and Shorter Schedule of Cost Components for ECC3 is given in Fig. 2.5. You can see from the side-by-side comparison of the two schedules that notionally they should provide the same answer; therefore, the box for the full SCC and the Shorter SCC are shown as being the same proportional size.

The biggest area of difference between the two schedules is how the components of cost for people and Equipment are treated.

2.13.1 People The Shorter SCC uses a people percentage whereas the full SCC uses a Working Areas overhead percentage, both of which are inserted by the *Contractor* at the time of tender in Contract Data part two.

The people percentage (Shorter SCC) covers the following items which are included separately in the full SCC:

- the shortfall in people items covered in the full SCC for items 12 and 13, for example 12(d) and (e), 13(c) to (n),[213]
- the Working Areas overheads percentage added to the cost of people in the full SCC as listed under Charges 44,
- charges as listed in the full SCC items 41, 42 and 43 which are included as individual cost components in the full SCC.

[211]Clause 51.3.
[212]ECC2 clause 63.11; ECC3 clause 63.15.
[213](c) to (o) in ECC3.

Full SSC	Shorter SCC
1. People FULL LIST OF COMPONENTS ('All-in' rate) 11, 12 and 13	**1. People** SHORTENED LIST OF COMPONENTS 11, 12 and 13 The percentage for **People** overheads is .... % (Contract Data part two) Includes • People items which are not included in the Shorter Schedule of people Components 11, 12 and 13 when compared to the full SCC
The percentage for Working Areas overheads is.............. % (Contract Data part two)	• FULL SCC AND INCLUDES Working Areas overhead (included in people percentage)
4. Charges (items 41, 42 and 43 included as separate items). Items listed in 44 are included in the Working Area overhead %	• **Charges** (included in people percentage)
2. Equipment Market hire rates or if internal, surrogate hire rate	**2. Equipment** Priced using FCEC (CECA) or RICS Dayworks adjusted to represent market hire rates (Equipment Adjustment % stated in Contract Data part two)
3. Plant and Materials (at cost) (the same as SSCC)	**3. Plant and Materials** (at cost) (the same as FSCC)
5. Manufacture and fabrication outside the Working Areas (Manufacture and fabrication overhead % from Contract Data part two) (the same as SSCC)	**5. Manufacture and fabrication outside the Working Areas** (Manufacture and fabrication overhead % from Contract Data part two) (the same as FSCC)
6. Design outside of the Working Areas (Design overheads from Contract Data part two) (the same as SSCC)	**6. Design outside of the Working Areas** (Design overheads from Contract Data part two) (the same)
7. Insurances (the same as SSCC)	**7. Insurances** (the same as FSCC)
***Contractor's* risk** (clause 63.5) *Compensation events only*	***Contractor's* risk** (clause 63.5) *Compensation events only*
The **Fee** (The *fee percentage* is ...... Contract Data part two) (the same)	The **Fee** (The *fee percentage* is ...... Contract Data part two) (the same)

Fig. 2.4. Diagram showing the components of Actual Cost for the full and Shorter Schedule of Cost Components – ECC2 only

Due to the greater coverage it is therefore evident and a useful check to ensure that the people percentage entered in Contract Data part two should be greater than the percentage for Working Area overheads inserted for the FSCC in Contract Data part two.

It is also apparent that the *Contractor* takes a greater risk with the Shorter SCC, since the people percentage has to include more items than are individually listed in the full SCC. Hence the suggestion that it is used for changes of a simpler nature.

2.13.2 Equipment The components of cost are the amounts listed in the published list inserted by the *Contractor* in the Contract Data or the list of Equipment inserted in the Contract Data for items of Equipment not on a published list.

2.14 Practical issues

2.14.1 Working on multiple projects on the same site The ECC SCC does not necessarily cater very well for contracts where there are many contractors on the same site. Because many of the percentages are based on projected turnover and the costs of the site, the *Contractor* may only be able to be realistic with percentages if the *Employer* has advised him of the projects that the *Contractor* will be performing over a period.

Full SCC	Shorter SCC

1. People
Directly employed people
Cost Components 11, 12 and 13
• Directly employed people
  • Whose normal place of work is the Working Area
  • Whose normal place of work is not the Working Area
Non-direct
Cost Component 14
	1. People
	Directly employed people
	Cost Components 11
	• Directly employed people
	  • Whose normal place of work is the Working Area
	  • Whose normal place of work is not the Working Area
	  • Not directly employed, but who are paid while they are in the Working Area

Working Areas overheads (Charges 44) The percentage for Working Area overheads is ....% (Contract Data part two)	**People overhead percentage (Charges 41)** The percentage for people overheads is ....% (Contract Data part two)
2. Equipment 21 Hire or rent of Equipment not owned by *Contractor* 22 Equipment not listed in the Contract Data but owned by the *Contractor* 23 Equipment purchased for the contract 24 Special Equipment 25 Consumables 26 Transporting, etc. 27 Materials to fabricate Equipment 28 Cost of operatives	**2. Equipment** 21 Published list (e.g. CECA) 22 List stated in Contract Data + 23 time calculation 27 Open market rates for Equipment not in published list or list stated in the Contract Data 25 Consumables 24 Transporting, etc. (no equivalent) 26 Cost of operatives
3. Plant and Materials (at cost) (the same as SSCC)	**3. Plant and Materials** (at cost) (the same as FSCC)

4. Charges
The following charges are identified separately:
41 Water, gas and electricity
 	
44 Working Area overhead % added to People cost components 11, 12, 13 and 14
42 Public authorities
43 (a) to (j) cancellation charges, etc.
	4. Charges
	41 People percentage, includes:
	  • Water, gas and electricity
	  • Buying or leasing land, compensation for loss of crops or buildings (clauses 43(b) to (g) of FSCC)
	  • Working Area overheads (clause 44 of FSCC)
	43 Public authorities
	42 Cancellation charges (clause 43(a) of FSCC)
	44 Consumables (clause 43(i) of FSCC)
	45 Specialist services (clause 43(h) of FSCC)

5. Manufacture and fabrication outside of the Working Areas Manufacture and fabrication overhead percentage from Contract Data part two	**5. Manufacture and fabrication outside of the Working Areas** Amounts paid to the *Contractor*
6. Design outside of the Working Areas Design overhead percentage from Contract Data part two (the same as SSCC)	**6. Design outside of the Working Areas** Design overhead percentage from Contract Data part two (the same as FSCC)
7. Insurance Deducted from cost • Costs against which contract required the Contractor to insure • Other costs paid to the *Contractor* by insurers (the same as SSCC)	**7. Insurance** Deducted from cost • Costs against which contract required the Contractor to insure • Other costs paid to the *Contractor* by insurers (the same as FSCC)
Compensation events only *Contractor*'s risks – clause 63.6	**Compensation events only** *Contractor*'s risks – clause 63.6
The Fee *Fee percentage* stated in Contract Data part two	**The Fee** *Direct fee percentage* and *subcontract fee percentage*, as stated in Contract Data part two

Fig. 2.5. Diagram showing the components of Defined Cost for the full and Shorter Schedule of Cost Components – ECC3 only

For site establishment costs[214] in particular, projects that overlap in time would necessarily impact on costs. The Working Area overhead percentage[215] is most affected since it is a function of the number of people on site, but could refer to the same site establishment that is used for all the concurrent projects. The total site establishment costs that would have been dissolved into a percentage applicable to people costs will be spread over two or more projects and clearly each project cannot carry the full cost for the site establishment

[214]Those cost components described in 44 of the full SCC and 4 (ECC3 41) of the Shorter SCC.
[215]And the percentage for people overheads for the Shorter SCC.

Table 2.8. Site overheads broken down on a project-by-project basis

		Total number of men split between projects			
		Month 1	Month 2	Month 3	Month 4
	Project 1	30	30	30	10
	Project 2	40	30	10	0
	Project 3	0	0	40	20
	Project 4	0	0	0	20
A	Number of men	**70**	**60**	**80**	**50**
		Percentage of men on each project			
		Month 1	Month 2	Month 3	Month 4
	Project 1	42.86	50.00	37.50	20.00
	Project 2	57.14	50.00	12.50	0.00
	Project 3	0	0	50.00	40.00
	Project 4	0	0	0	40.00
B	Total %	100.00	100.00	100.00	100.00
		Total site establishment cost of £70,000.00 per month split between the projects based on percentage breakdown given above			
		Month 1	Month 2	Month 3	Month 4
	Project 1	£30,000	£35,000	£26,250	£14,000
	Project 2	£40,000	£35,000	£8,750	0
	Project 3	0	0	£35,000	£28,000
	Project 4	0	0	0	£28,000
C	Total	**£70,000**	**£70,000**	**£70,000**	**£70,000**

costs. There are a number of ways of dealing with this problem, and no doubt organisations will have their own preference. Two methods are described below.

The total Actual Cost[216] of site establishment in pounds sterling could be divided between the projects in a ratio concomitant with their size and value. This is to avoid all the costs being charged to one project and none to others so that one project's budget is not adversely affected. This choice would mean altering the wording in the Schedule of Cost Components and the data required in Contract Data part two, since the percentage would no longer be required.

A second choice, and one that tends to be more preferable to *Employers*, is to apply a percentage of a percentage. The primary percentage – that is, the Working Area overhead percentage – would remain. This would be based on the total labour on site across all projects to represent the site establishment costs experienced by the *Contractor*. Through all these calculations it should be realised that an increase or decrease in projects may require a corresponding increase or decrease in the site establishment required and so the primary percentage could change, as mentioned above in the section dealing with the Working Area overhead percentage. Each month, a percentage is applied that focuses each project on the number of men for each project and therefore the amount of site establishment that should be carried by each project.

Table 2.8 shows how this may operate based on the following data:

Total labour = 70 men across two projects initially.

Total Site establishment costs per month = £70,000.00 across all projects.

2.14.2 Example of the principles of the assessment of change A new retaining wall is to be constructed as shown in Fig. 2.6. This is a retaining wall on an *Employer*-designed project. It is realised, however, that the length of the retaining wall needs to be increased from 10 m to 20 m. The

[216]Supported by appropriate documentation.

0.300 m

Note: Overall length of reinforced concrete retaining wall to be 10 m

1.500 m

100 mm uPVC drainage channels at 1 m centres

0.400 m

1.000 m

Fig. 2.6. Cross-section through reinforced concrete retaining wall

Project Manager acknowledges that this is a change to the Works Information, and raises an instruction and compensation event notification in which he asks the *Contractor* to submit a quotation.

Table 2.9 shows three possible scenarios A, B and C.

The main Option for the contract is Option A.[217] The correct tendered price for the work is £2000 as shown in scenario B below. In scenario A, the *Contractor* has underpriced the true value of the original work in his tender and has inserted £1000. In scenario C a high price has been inserted of £3000. It should be noted that the prices against individual items should be set against the context of the pricing for the whole contract. The example of low, correct and high is given here for illustrative purposes on the principles of the SCC.

For the purposes of assessing the changes to the Prices from a compensation event to change the length of the retaining wall, the original tendered prices of Low £1000 in scenario A, Correct £2000 in scenario B and High £3000 in scenario C are not used. Instead the original work and the revised work are priced using the Schedule of Cost Components.

In this example as shown below in Table 2.9, the assessment of the original work using the Schedule of Cost Components will give a true assessment of £2000 in all three scenarios. This figure is then compared to the assessment of the revised work to the retaining wall of £4000 in each scenario; taking one

Table 2.9. SCC low, correct and high price scenarios

	Scenario A	Scenario B	Scenario C
Tendered prices			
Item	**Low price**	**Correct price**	**High price**
Original retaining wall (This could be a price for an activity in an *activity schedule* or a *bills of quantities* item)	£1000	£2000	£3000
Total	**£1000**	**£2000**	**£3000**
Assessment of change using the Schedule of Cost Components			
Assessment of original work	£2000	£2000	£2000
Assessment of revised work	£4000	£4000	£4000
Total of the changes to the Prices	**£2000**	**£2000**	**£2000**

[217]The same principles would work for Option B as well.

from the other gives a total change to the Prices of £2000 in all three scenarios.

In each scenario the outcome is the same when using the SCC to assess the changes to the Prices by omitting the original work and adding in the revised work, so that the outcome is the same in each instance. This therefore removes the arguments about the use and applicability of rates, prices and lump sums submitted at the time of tender.

2.14.3 Omissions   If an *Employer* omits work from a contract, the omission will be assessed using the SCC rather than simply omitting the relevant sums in the *activity schedule* or the *bill of quantities*. The build-up for the omission in the form of a quotation will include the tendered *fee percentage* (ECC3 *direct fee percentage*).

This raises the issue of loss of profit on omitted work for the *Contractor*. The ECC is simply silent on this matter. From a practical point of view small omissions are of little consequence, unless they build up to such an extent that they become a large change or omission to the scope of the works. Larger omissions, which affect the overall scope of the *works*, are a different matter.

The ECC is based on the concept of the *Employer* planning his works well. Nevertheless, circumstances do occur when, no matter how well planned a project, the project is overtaken by events. Let us consider an example where the *Employer* owns a complex of buildings on one site.

The project involves the construction of a new five-storey office block, which is to be linked to an existing office block by a subway under the site link road to an existing basement entrance in the existing office (see Fig. 2.7). This connection to the existing office block has been identified as a separate activity on the *activity schedule* on an Option A contract.

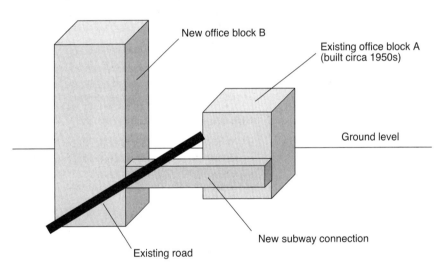

Fig. 2.7. Office block scheme

Twelve months into the project the *Employer*'s facilities management team has identified that, due to rapid growth, the existing office facilities need to be increased to cope with this growth. It has also been identified that the existing office facilities are also now below modern standards and they have recommended that the existing office block is demolished and a new office built in its place.

The *Employer* has also decided that it would be more appropriate and less disruptive to his operations on site if the subway connection were repackaged into the new project. The work on the subway is still some six months away.

The *Project Manager* issues an instruction and compensation event notification omitting the new subway. The *Contractor* sends a quotation, which equals the value of £250,000.00 as shown on his *activity schedule* for the project.

The *Project Manager* rejects the quotation and instructs the *Contractor* to provide a revised quotation. The reason given is that the quotation is not in accordance with clause 63.1, namely that that quotation has not been assessed on:

- the Actual Cost (ECC3 the actual Defined Cost) of the work already done,
- the forecast Actual Cost (ECC3 Defined Cost) of the work yet to be done,
- the resulting Fee.

The *Contractor* resubmits his quotation on this basis and in accordance with the contract. The total omission is £243,348.00. This is the amount by which the Prices would be reduced according to the compensation event, rather than the £250,000 originally included in the *activity schedule*.

2.14.4 *Project Manager's* assessment

The contract contains within it the facility for the *Project Manager* to make his own assessment. If we imagine in the office block example that the *Contractor* refuses to provide a revised quotation then the *Project Manager* can make his own assessment (see also section 1.9.1 of Chapter 1 above). The *Project Manager's* assessment comes to £298,000.00. This means that the amount by which the Prices would be reduced according to the compensation event would be £298,000, rather than the £250,000 originally included in the *activity schedule* (always remembering that the price inserted against an activity may not be reflective of its true price). Since the reduction is larger than the originally included figure, it could be assumed that the *Contractor's* profit will be affected by this compensation event.

The figure of £298,000 is substantially higher than the one the *Contractor* would have come to if he had done the quotation himself. It should be noted that the *Project Manager* does not have to instruct the *Contractor* to resubmit his quotation, he could go straight to a *Project Manager's* assessment. It is unwise for the *Contractor* to get to such a point, since the *Project Manager* will not have the same level of information in regard to the compensation event as the *Contractor* himself.

This being the case, and as long as he demonstrates that he has built up the quotation as required by the contract using reasonable skill and care, there is no reason why his assessment should not be acceptable.

Areas, which will have a major influence on the assessment, are:

- programme durations,
- output levels,
- critical path,
- resource levelling either on the whole or parts of the *works* for both people and Equipment.

If a *Contractor* submits a quotation which is not in accordance with the requirements of the contract, the *Project Manager* can make his own assessment.

It is not a requirement of the contract that the *Project Manager* give the *Contractor* an opportunity to resubmit a quotation before he makes his own assessment.

2.14.5 Numerous small compensation events

The ECC assumes that every compensation event is assessed individually. However, on the hurly-burly of everyday projects this is rarely the case. Sometimes once one thing goes wrong or a dimension is changed it triggers a whole sequence of events, albeit each one being very minor.

In such instance it may be appropriate for a number of these small compensation events on related items to be grouped and assessed together – see Table 2.10. In this way it is possible to identify any possible knock-on effects which may not be evident from each single small compensation event. It will also facilitate picking up what has been traditionally called the 'disruption' element of change.

Table 2.10. Compensation events grouped together for assessment

		Lift shaft A		
PMI No.	CE No.	Description	Effect	
			Time (days or part of)	Prices (£)
1	3	Additional reinforcement to waling beam A	0.25	1000.00
4	7	Missing rebar to waling beam B	0.50	500.00
8	9	Cut rebar on site to revised dimensions	0.75	500.00
		Total	1.50 days	2000.00

2.14.6 Issue of Site Information drawings

The *Project Manager* issues an instruction containing some revised Site Information drawings labelled 'For Information Purposes Only'.

The issue of Site Information drawings in itself is not a compensation event unless the issue of that information requires a change to the Works Information, in which case it will be a compensation event.

Project Managers should be mindful to issue only relevant Site Information drawings and not just issue a blanket set of Site Information drawings. Hopefully, the *Project Manager* will have reviewed the drawings to see if they have or are likely to have any implications on the Works Information.

2.14.7 Occasions when Actual/ Defined Cost is not used

There are certain occasions when the contract does not call for the use of Actual/Defined Cost as defined in the SCC.

2.14.7.1 Uncorrected Defects

If a notified Defect is not corrected, the *Project Manager* assesses **the cost** of having the Defect corrected by other people. The **cost** will be whatever that is as assessed by the *Project Manager*.

> The *Project Manager* notifies the *Contractor* that he has not corrected the Defective plasterwork in the entrance area of the new hotel within the *defect correction period*.
>
> The *Project Manager* therefore assesses the **cost** of having the Defect corrected by other people and advises the *Contractor* of this fact.

2.14.7.2 Possession of the Site (ECC3: Access to the Site)

Any cost incurred by the *Employer* as a result of the *Contractor* not providing the facilities and services he is to provide is assessed by the *Project Manager* and paid by the *Contractor*.

> In the section for facilities and services to be provided by the *Contractor*, the Works Information requires the *Contractor* to provide a cleaner for the site accommodation. After four weeks of the contract no cleaner has appeared, even after repeated requests by the *Project Manager*.
>
> The *Project Manager* advises the *Contractor* that he has hired a cleaner for the duration of the contract or until such time as he provides the cleaner as required by the Works Information.
>
> The *Project Manager* has assessed this cost to be £20 per day and he advises the *Contractor* that he will be required to pay this cost as detailed in clause 33.2.

2.14.7.3 Tests and inspections The cost incurred by the *Employer* in repeating tests after a Defect is found is assessed by the *Project Manager* and paid by the *Contractor*.

> The *Contractor* offers up some completed watermain pipework as being completed and free from Defects. The Works Information requires the *Employer* to carry out water tests on the pipework. The pipework fails the test.
>
> A week later the pipework, after being corrected, is retested and passes the *Employer*'s test.
>
> The *Project Manager* notifies the *Contractor* that he has assessed the costs incurred by the *Employer* in redoing the test and advises that £896.00 is to be paid by the *Contractor*.

2.14.7.4 Acceleration If the *Project Manager* has instructed the *Contractor* to submit a quotation for acceleration and the *Contractor* chooses to do so, the quotation he submits is not required to be based on Actual/Defined Cost.

> The SCC is a list of admissible components of cost under the ECC.
>
> The Shorter SCC is for use on changes of a simple nature.

> **Question**
>
> A *Project Manager* becomes aware after contract is let that the data for the FSCC and SSCC in Contract Data part two have not been completed or that the *Contractor* is struggling to complete the information. What should he do?
>
> **Solution**
>
> Strictly this is the *Contractor*'s problem; however, his failing to understand the SCC may cause problems later in the project. So it may be in the interests of all involved to ensure that he has understood the requirements of the contract.

2.14.7.5 Quotations manual The cost of people involved in a compensation event is based on the components of cost for people listed in the schedule of cost components. If there are few compensation events then this process is straightforward. However if you have many compensation events the calculation of people costs for each and every compensation event may be very time consuming. To overcome this it may be more practical to establish a quotations manual in which the initial people rates (and other components of cost) have been agreed and calculated using the schedule of cost components at the outset of the contract. This has the advantages of:

- establishing agreed rates at the outset of the contract
- provide consistency on multiple Sites/administration sites
- speeds up the assessment of compensation events.

2.14.7.6 Disallowed Cost Finally, recognising the *Employers* potential vulnerability under cost-based contracts, the ECC includes the concept of **Disallowed Cost**, a full and lengthy definition of which is provided at Main Option Clause ~~11.2(30)~~ (ECC3: 11.2(25)). Generically, the definition is a list of things for which the *Contractor* will not be reimbursed i.e. any costs incurred against the headings identified will be deducted from ~~Actual~~/Defined Cost. Most of the things included could be said to derive from some 'shortcoming' of the *Contractor* or failure to conduct his operations to acceptable standards. This immediately introduces an element of discretion, which falls to be exercised by the *Project Manager*, a subject which has recently turned the spotlight on the *Project Manager*'s implied duty to act impartially and in good faith. Examples of Disallowed Cost include:

- cost which the *Project Manager* decides is not justified by the *Contractor*'s accounts and records;
- the cost of correcting Defects after Completion;
- Plant and Materials not used to Provide the Works (after allowing for reasonable wastage); and
- resources not used to Provide the Works (after allowing for reasonable availability and utilisation) or not taken away from the Working Areas when the *Project Manager* requested.

Although payments to Subcontractors for work which is subcontracted constitute Actual/Defined Cost, lest *Contractors* run away with the idea that their administration of subcontracts need be to some lesser standard, Disallowed Cost includes the following Subcontractor-specific checks:

- cost which the *Project Manager* decides should not have been paid to a Subcontractor in accordance with his Subcontract; and
- cost which the *Project Manager* decides results from paying a Subcontractor more for a compensation event than is included in the accepted quotation or assessment for the compensation event.

So, given that the *Contractor* is clearly at risk that some of his Actual/Defined Cost will not be reimbursed, how should he cover himself against this eventuality, given for example that some Disallowed Cost is almost inevitable e.g. the cost of correcting Defects after Completion. The answer whilst simple is not always obvious. Any Actual/Defined Cost which the *Contractor* anticipates incurring but which may be the subject of a Disallowed Cost deduction has to be recovered through the Fee and consequently the *fee percentage* will need to include an allowance for protecting against this risk. Clearly, some *Employers,* depending on their choice of *Project Manager* will be regarded by *Contractors* as more 'risky' than Others and this may be reflected in the tendered *fee percentage.*

2.15 Preliminaries and people costs

2.15.1 Introduction Appendix 3 provides practical examples of how people costs are built up and how the traditional calculation compares to the full and Shorter Schedules of Cost Components, and how this relates to the *fee percentage* (ECC3: direct fee percentage) and percentage for people overheads.

Appendix 4 gives a comparison of a traditional preliminaries build-up and the full and Shorter Schedule of Cost Components.

Both these appendices serve to clarify the interrelationship between traditional practice and the ECC.

Appendix 2

Section A – ECC2

Example quotations for compensation events

(Based on the full Schedule of Cost Components and Shorter Schedule of Cost Components)

Section B – ECC3

Example quotations for compensation events

(Based on the full Schedule of Cost Components and Shorter Schedule of Cost Components)

Section A – ECC2 only

Example quotations for compensation events

(Based on the full Schedule of Cost Components (FSCC) and Shorter Schedule of Cost Components (SSCC))

A2.1 Introduction

This is an example of a quotation for a hypothetical compensation event on a project named Spring Field. The compensation event is for the provision of a new footbridge over the existing Spring Dyke following the realignment of Spring Road. For the purposes of this example it is assumed that the new footbridge will be a new section of works (created by a supplemented agreement) to the existing contract for Spring Field.

The contract has been let on a main Option A Priced Contract with Activity Schedule.

This example sets out a format for the presentation of the quotation and includes build-ups, supporting notes and comments on some of the issues surrouhding the preparation of quotations.

Figure A2.1 shows a sectional view of the proposed new footbridge. A programme for the works has been prepared and is shown in Fig. A2.2. (Note that for section A of this appendix the sections, figures and tables are numbered with a prefix A and for section B with a prefix B.)

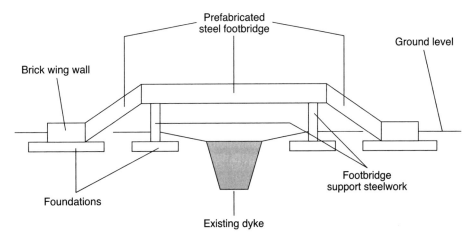

Fig. A2.1. Proposed new footbridge over Spring Dyke

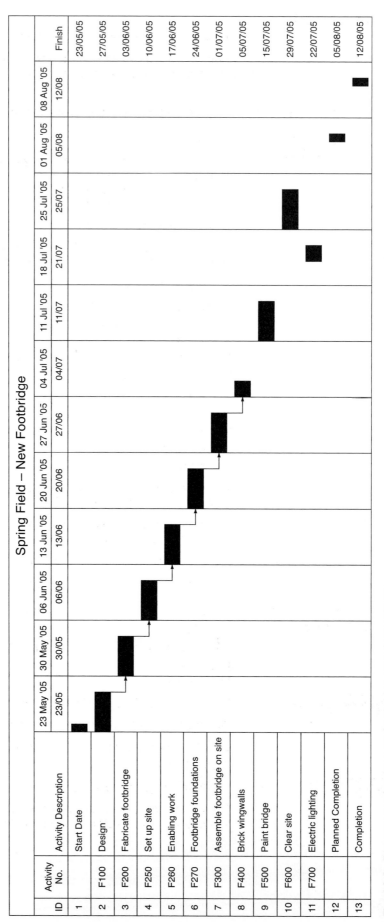

Fig. A2.2. Programme for the new footbridge over Spring Dyke

A2.2 Example quotation

The following is an example of a quotation for the new footbridge.

The Contract Data part two extracted from the documents which are part of the contract used to produce this example quotation is shown below.

Contract Data part two – Data provided by the *Contractor*

Statements given in all contracts

- The *Contractor* is

Name	Virtual Contracting Limited
Address	Virtual House
	Virtual Lane
	Virtual City

- The *fee percentage* is 10%.

- The *working areas* are the Site and the area indicated on drawing FYK001 as lay-down and prefabrication facilities.

- The key people are:

(1) Name	Joe Bloggs
Job	Site Agent
Responsibilities	....
Qualifications	....
Experience	....
(2) Name	John Public
Job	QS
Responsibilities	....
Qualifications	....
Experience	....

- The Works Information for the *Contractor*'s design is in the document entitled 'Contractor's Proposal'.

- The programme identified in the Contract Data is in the document entitled 'Contractor's Programme'.

Option A

- The *activity schedule* is in the document entitled 'Activity Schedule'.

- The tendered total of the Prices is £1,843,000.

Data for Schedule of Cost Components

- The hourly rates for Actual Cost of manufacture or fabrication outside the Working Areas are

Category of employee	Hourly rate
Foreman	£20
Fabricators	£20

  Note: See example build-up in A2.3.5.

- The percentage for manufacture or fabrication overheads is 20%.

- The hourly rates for Actual Cost of design outside the Working Areas are:

Category of employee	Hourly rate
Draughtsman	£30

  Note: See example build-up in A2.3.6.

- The percentage for design overheads is 30%.

- The categories of employees whose travelling expenses to and from the Working Areas are included in Actual Cost are NONE.

Not used with the Shorter Schedule of Cost Components

Note: See example build-up in A2.3.3.

Note: See Table A2.2 for example calculation.

Only used with the Shorter Schedule of Cost Components

- Except for special items the percentage for Equipment depreciation and maintenance is 25%.

- The percentages for depreciation and maintenance for special items of Equipment are:

Equipment	Size or capacity	%
Tunnel boring machine	2 tonnes	33%

- The percentage for Working Areas overheads is 12%.

- The percentage for **People** overheads is 31%.

- The published list of Equipment is the last edition of the list published by CECA.

- The percentage for adjustment for listed Equipment is −30%.

- The rates of other Equipment are:

Equipment	Size or capacity	Rate
N/A..	....	....
....	....	....
....	....	....

CONTRACT: SPRING FIELD

QUOTATION FOR COMPENSATION EVENT

To: Project Manager	No: 41	*Note: The Activity Numbers should relate to the activity schedule and the Accepted Programme.*
From: Virtual Contracting Limited	Sheet: 1	
Brief Description of Works: Provision of Footbridge to Spring Dyke Due to Road Realignment	Date: 1 July 2005	
ACTIVITY NO./NOS: **F100 to F700**	**DELAY TO PLANNED COMPLETION:** **1 Day**	SECTION OF WORKS AFFECTED: **3A**

1 PEOPLE

Activity F250 – Set up site (5 days)

Effect on overall planned Completion should be stated here. In this particular example it is assumed that this work can be undertaken concurrently with the main works. Details for calculating the cost of people.

See supporting notes section A2.3.1 and section A2.3.2 sample calculation for calculating the cost of people.

	No.	Hrs	Total Hrs	Rate		
Foreman	1	24	24	15.00	360.00	
Labourers	4	40	160	10.51	1,681.60	
Ganger	1	40	40	8.00	320.00	2,361.60

Activity F260 – Enabling Work (5 days)

	No.	Hrs	Total Hrs	Rate		
Foreman	1	16	16	15.00	240.00	
Labourers	3	40	120	10.51	1,261.20	1,501.20

Activity F270 – Footbridge Foundations (5 days)

	No.	Hrs	Total Hrs	Rate		
Foreman	1	40	40	15.00	600.00	
Labourers	3	50	150	10.51	1,576.50	
Ganger	1	40	40	8.00	320.00	2,496.50

Activity F300 – Assemble Footbridge on site (5 days)

	No.	Hrs	Total Hrs	Rate		
Foreman	1	50	50	15.00	750.00	
Ganger	1	50	50	8.00	400.00	
Steel fixers	4	50	200	12.00	2,400.00	
Crane operator	1	50	50	12.00	600.00	
Banksman	1	50	50	11.00	550.00	
Labourers	2	50	100	10.51	1,051.00	5,751.00

PEOPLE c/f						£12,110.30

CONTRACT: SPRING FIELD		
QUOTATION FOR COMPENSATION EVENT		
To: Project Manager	No: 41	
From: Virtual Contracting Limited	Sheet: 2	
Brief Description of Works: Provision of Footbridge to Spring Dyke Due to Road Realignment	Date: 1 July 2005	

ACTIVITY NO./NOS: **F100 to F700**	DELAY TO PLANNED COMPLETION: **1 Day**	SECTION OF WORKS AFFECTED: **3A**

						PEOPLE b/f		£12,110.30
Activity F400 – Brick Wingwalls (2 days)								
	No.	*Days*	*Total days*	*×Hrs*	*Total Hrs*	*Rate*		
Foreman	1	2	2	10	20	15.00	300.00	
Bricklayers	4	2	8	10	80	12.00	960.00	
Labourer	2	2	4	10	40	10.51	420.40	1,680.40
Activity F500 – Paint Bridge (5 days)								
	No.	*Days*	*Total days*	*×Hrs*	*Total Hrs*	*Rate*		
Painters	2	5	10	10	100	12.00	1,200.00	1,200.00
Activity F600 – Clear Site (5 days)								
	No.	*Days*	*Total days*	*×Hrs*	*Total Hrs*	*Rate*		
Foreman	1	5	5	8	40	15.00	600.00	
Labourer	2	5	10	10	100	10.51	1,051.00	1,651.00
Activity No. F100 *Site Staff Costs – Preparation of Quotation*								
					Hrs	*Rate*		
QS					10	25.00	250.00	
Engineer E1					8	25.00	200.00	
Buyer					7	20.00	140.00	
Site Agent					5	35.00	175.00	
Planner					4	30.00	120.00	885.00
PEOPLE c/f								£17,526.70

> Note that for Options A and B, the preparation of quotations is not an allowable cost (clause 11.2(28)).

CONTRACT: SPRING FIELD		
QUOTATION FOR COMPENSATION EVENT		
To: Project Manager	No: 41	
From: Virtual Contracting Limited	Sheet: 3	
Brief Description of Works: Provision of Footbridge to Spring Dyke Due to Road Realignment	Date: 1 July 2005	
ACTIVITY NO./NOS: **F100 to F700**	DELAY TO PLANNED COMPLETION: **1 Day**	SECTION OF WORKS AFFECTED: 3A

					PEOPLE b/f		£17,526.70

Activity F260 – Enabling Work
(5 days)

Supervision of the erection of temporary works by Head Office –
temporary works supervisor.

> Note: Head office cost should be recovered through *fee percentage*.

Team Leader					1 day	80.00	
Inspection of the erected temporary works by Independent Third Party					1 day	150.00	230.00

Activity F700 – Electric Lighting (Spring Electrics)
(2 days)

> Note: This information should be available from the Subcontractor's quotation to the *Contractor*.

	No.	Days	Total days	×Hrs	Total Hrs	Rate		
Foreman	1	2	2	10	20	20.00	400.00	
Electrician	4	2	8	10	80	15.00	1,200.00	
Trainee electrician	1	2	2	10	20	7.00	140.00	1,740.00

> See sample calculation in attached supporting notes in section A2.3.3. Consideration may also need to be given to whether this percentage is appropriate given that this is a new section of *works*. Includes an absorption of Subcontractor's Working Areas overheads as shown in example subcontractor's quotation.

Subtotal	19,496.70
Working Areas overhead + 12%	2,339.60
PEOPLE TOTAL CARRIED TO SUMMARY	£21,836.30

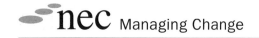

CONTRACT: SPRING FIELD	
QUOTATION FOR COMPENSATION EVENT	
To: Project Manager	No: 41
From: Virtual Contracting Limited	Sheet: 4
Brief Description of Works: Provision of Footbridge to Spring Dyke Due to Road Realignment	Date: 1 July 2005

ACTIVITY NO./NOS: **F100 to F700**	DELAY TO PLANNED COMPLETION: **1 Day**	SECTION OF WORKS AFFECTED: **3A**

2 EQUIPMENT

> Note: See example calculation for amount for depreciation and maintenance charge in section A2.3.4 of attached supporting notes.

Activity F250 – Set up Site
(5 days)
Contractors owned equipment

Dumper	5 days	10/12th wk	@	£50/wk	41.67	
Hired Equipment						
Lorry	5 days	@	100	day	500.00	
Shovel				say	10.00	
Hand-saw				say	20.00	571.67

> Note: See full SCC item 44 (q).

Activity F260 – Enabling Work
(5 days)

Dumper	5 days	10/12th wk	@	£50/wk	41.67	
Hired Equipment						
Lorry	5 days	@	100	day	500.00	
Excavator	5 days	@	200	day	1000.00	1,541.67

> Note: Ensure that the Equipment rate excludes the people cost – see FSCC item 25.

Activity F270 – Footbridge Foundations
(5 days)

Dumper	5 days	10/12th wk	@	£50/wk	41.67	
Hired Equipment						
Concrete mixer	5 days	@	20	day	100.00	
Wheelbarrow	5 days	@	5	day	25.00	166.67

EQUIPMENT c/f	£2,280.01

CONTRACT: SPRING FIELD							
QUOTATION FOR COMPENSATION EVENT							
To: Project Manager					No: 41		
From: Virtual Contracting Limited					Sheet: 5		
Brief Description of Works: Provision of Footbridge to Spring Dyke Due to Road Realignment					Date: 1 July 2005		
ACTIVITY NO./NOS: **F100 to F700**		DELAY TO PLANNED COMPLETION: **1 Day**			SECTION OF WORKS AFFECTED: **3A**		

			EQUIPMENT b/f				£2,280.01
Activity F300 – Assemble Footbridge on Site (2 days)							
Dumper	2 days	4/12th wk	@		£25/wk	16.67	
Lorry	1 day	@		100	day	100.00	
Hired Equipment							
Crane (inc. driver, delivery and removal from site)	2 days	@		50	day	100.00	
Setting out equipment					say	40.00	256.67
Activity F400 – Brick Wingwalls (2 days)							
Dumper	2 days	4/12th wk	@		£25/wk	16.67	
Hired Equipment							
Lorry	2 days	@		100	day	200.00	
Concrete mixer	2 days	@		20	day	40.00	256.67
Activity F500 – Paint Bridge (5 days)							
Hired Equipment							
Trestles	5 days	@		10	day	50.00	50.00
Activity F600 – Clear Site (5 days)							
Dumper	7 days	4/12th wk	@		£25/wk	58.33	
Hired Equipment							
Lorry	5 days	@		100	day	495.02	553.35
EQUIPMENT c/f							£3,396.70

Note: Inclusion of driver with crane. If inserted here you will not recover in the Working Area overhead percentage as well.

Note: These types of items may need to be listed in Contract Data part two.

nec Managing Change

CONTRACT: SPRING FIELD			
QUOTATION FOR COMPENSATION EVENT			

To: Project Manager	No: 41
From: Virtual Contracting Limited	Sheet: 6
Brief Description of Works: Provision of Footbridge to Spring Dyke Due to Road Realignment	Date: 1 July 2005

ACTIVITY NO./NOS: **F100 to F700**	DELAY TO PLANNED COMPLETION: **1 Day**	SECTION OF WORKS AFFECTED: **3A**

EQUIPMENT b/f			£3,396.70
Activity F250 – Set up site Consumables — Note: See FSCC item 23.			
• Sacrificial framework 10 sheets	@ £20	200.00	
• Fuel for Generator 10 litres	@ 80p/litre	8.00	
• Transporting crane to and from Working Areas		100.00	308.00
Note: See FSCC item 24(a).			
EQUIPMENT TOTAL CARRIED TO SUMMARY =			£3,704.70
3 PLANT AND MATERIALS			
Activity F200 – Fabricate Footbridge			
Materials for Footbridge			
• Durasteel	100 m^2 @ £50	5,000.00	
• RSA 45 × 45mm	100 m @ £5	500.00	
• Black bolts	500 No. @ £2	1,000.00	
• Stainless steel handrails	60 m @ £100	6,000.00	12,500.00
Activity F270 – Footbridge Foundations			
Concrete	80 m^3 @ £50	4,000.00	
Formwork	20 sheets @ £20	400.00	4,400.00
Activity F400 – Brick Wing walls			
Bricks	2000 No. @ £0.05p	100.00	
(Returned pallet)	(−£10)	(10.00)	
Brick sample	£50	50.00	140.00
PLANT & MATERIALS c/f			£17,040.00

    www.neccontract.com

CONTRACT: SPRING FIELD		
QUOTATION FOR COMPENSATION EVENT		

To: Project Manager	No: 41
From: Virtual Contracting Limited	Sheet: 7
Brief Description of Works: Provision of Footbridge to Spring Dyke Due to Road Realignment	Date: 1 July 2005

ACTIVITY NO./NOS: **F100 to F700**	DELAY TO PLANNED COMPLETION: **1 Day**	SECTION OF WORKS AFFECTED: **3A**

PLANT & MATERIALS b/f				£17,040.00
Activity F700 (supplied by Spring Electrics)				
Lights	20 No.	@	£100.00	2,000.00	
Cabling	180 m	@	£10.00/m	1,800.00	3,800.00
PLANT AND MATERIALS TOTAL CARRIED TO SUMMARY =				£20,840.00

4 CHARGES

Activity F250

1 Payment for temporary connection and disconnection of electrical supply to LEB (item 42)	50.00	
2 Payment for temporary connection charges by Water Authority (item 42)	50.00	
3 Local Authority inspection charge	50.00	
4 Payment to Mr Jones for access to the Working Area and loss of crops (item 43g and c)	500.00	650.00

Note: Items 44(a) to (q) are a list of charges for the provision and use of accommodation, equipment, supplies and services, within the Working Areas. These items are included in the percentage for Working Area overheads added to item 1. People as stated by the *Contractor* in Contract Data part two.

CHARGES TOTAL CARRIED TO SUMMARY =	£650.00

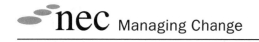
CONTRACT: SPRING FIELD	
QUOTATION FOR COMPENSATION EVENT	

To: Project Manager	No: 41
From: Virtual Contracting Limited	Sheet: 8
Brief Description of Works: Provision of Footbridge to Spring Dyke Due to Road Realignment	Date: 1 July 2005

ACTIVITY NO./NOS: **F100 to F700**	DELAY TO PLANNED COMPLETION: **1 Day**	SECTION OF WORKS AFFECTED: **3A**

5 MANUFACTURE AND FABRICATION

Activity F200 – Fabrication of Footbridge

Employee Costs

Foreman	5 days × 8 hrs	40	@	£20	800.00	
Fabricators, 8 men	5 days × 8 hrs	320	@	£20	6,400.00	7,200.00
Subtotal						7,200.00
Percentage for manufacturing and fabrication overheads stated in Contract Data part two +20%						1,440.00

MANUFACTURE AND FABRICATION TOTAL CARRIED TO SUMMARY =	£8,640.00

CONTRACT: SPRING FIELD		
QUOTATION FOR COMPENSATION EVENT		
To: Project Manager	No: 41	
From: Virtual Contracting Limited	Sheet: 9	
Brief Description of Works: Provision of Footbridge to Spring Dyke Due to Road Realignment	Date: 1 July 2005	
ACTIVITY NO./NOS: **F100 to F700**	DELAY TO PLANNED COMPLETION: **1 Day**	SECTION OF WORKS AFFECTED: **3A**

6   DESIGN

Activity F100 Design

(A)	*Employee Cost* Draughtsman, 4 men × 10 hrs per day × 5 days = 200 hrs @ £30	6,000.00	
(B)	Percentage for design overheads taken from Contract Data part two +30%	1,800.00	
(C)	Travel costs (in Contract Data part two included in employee hourly rate)	N/A	7,800.00
DESIGN TOTAL CARRIED TO SUMMARY =			**£7,800.00**

7   INSURANCE

Deduct from cost: • The cost of events which this contract requires the *Contractor* to insure and	N/A	
• Other costs paid by the insurer	N/A	
INSURANCE TOTAL CARRIED TO SUMMARY =		N/A

CONTRACT: SPRING FIELD	
QUOTATION FOR COMPENSATION EVENT	
To: Project Manager	No: 41
From: Virtual Contracting Limited	Sheet: 10
Brief Description of Works: Provision of Footbridge to Spring Dyke Due to Road Realignment	Date: 1 July 2005

ACTIVITY NO./NOS: **F100 to F700**	DELAY TO PLANNED COMPLETION: **1 Day**	SECTION OF WORKS AFFECTED: **3A**

SUMMARY	
1. PEOPLE	£21,836.30
2. EQUIPMENT	£3,704.70
3. PLANT AND MATERIALS	£20,840.00
4. CHARGES	£650.00
5. MANUFACTURE AND FABRICATION	£8,640.00
6. DESIGN	£7,800.00
7. INSURANCE	N/A
Subtotal	£63,471.00
8. Time Risk Allowances (see example in Table A2.4 below)	£0.00
Subtotal	**£63,471.00**
9. FEE Note: See an example of *fee percentages* calculation in Chapter 2. ——— *fee percentage* 10%	£6,347.10
TOTAL =	**£69,818.10**

A2.3 Supporting notes

The following supporting notes seek to amplify and support the example quotation given in section A2.2 above.

1   People – calculation of people (labour) costs
2   Example schedule of people rates from a quotations manual (see 1.15.8)
3   Calculation for Working Areas overhead percentage
4   Example calculation for percentage for Equipment depreciation and maintenance
5   Calculation of the percentage for manufacture and fabrication overheads
6   Calculation of the percentage for design overheads
7   *Contractor*'s risk
8   Subcontractors
9   Activity Schedule

A2.3.1 People – Calculation of people (labour) costs

The calculation of people costs is based upon:

- the Actual Cost (as defined by the Schedule of Cost Components) of the work already done; and
- the forecast Actual Cost of the work not yet done.

It is important to note that tender rates and prices are not used to assess change and in all instances the cost for the different grades of people involved will be based on:

- a payroll printout showing the required information,
- proof of other payments such as lodging allowances,
- other documentary evidence.

Table A2.1 shows a typical example of a contractor's payroll printout and a build-up for the cost of people based on the Components in the Schedule of Cost Components.

In theory this exercise, based on the *Contractor*'s accounts and records, is needed for each and every category of people on each and every quotation for a compensation event. This principle is adequate where compensation events are few and far between but on larger projects it may not be so practical.

Some employers and contractors have agreed on larger projects to do this exercise once a month or every quarter to establish a list of agreed rates to use for quotations. Some have developed what are called quotation manuals which are included at the time of tender to establish the first people costs and other costs for use to assess compensation events. This document is then reviewed every month and a set of project-wide rates for the month or period ahead is agreed. This is particularly useful on large, multi-location projects which have large teams of people on the project.

Although this is not strictly ECC, it is a practical way of providing consistency of approach across a project and reduces the need for too many people having to get involved in establishing the Actual Cost of people and reduces the fears of the *Contractor* in having to adopt an open-book approach on sensitive commercial information.

It also makes the audit of compensation events a great deal more simple.

A2.3.2 Example schedule of people rates from a quotations manual

Table A2.2 shows an extract from a quotations manual which shows the agreed hourly rates to be used in the assessment of compensation events during a month or period.

A2.3.3 Calculation for Working Areas overhead percentage

This percentage, added to the cost of people, covers the costs of the *Contractor*'s on-site overheads in his Working Areas.

The *Contractor*, at the time of tender, inserts in the Contract Data part two his required percentage for Working Area overheads. A typical list of items to be

Table A2.1. Example of a *Contractor*'s payroll

Payroll Build-up Based on Full Schedule of Cost Components			Traditional calculation of hourly rates for labour based on the Working Rule Agreement	
General Operative Mr X for Period 1: 4-week period from 1 to 30 June 2005			General Operative Mr X for Period 1: 4-week period from 1 to 30 June 2005	
11	**Wages and Salary** *(Figure made up of Basic Rate, Additional Payments for skill, National Insurance and Training Levy Allowance from traditional build-up opposite)* [Items marked with an asterisk]	1,161.21	Basic Rate of Pay (Classification – General Operative, Skill Rate 1, 2, 3, 4, Craft Rate) 213 hrs @ 4.78	1,018.14*
		0.00	Additional Payment for Skilled Work WRA (Schedule 1 – Classification i, ii, iii) 0 hrs @ 4.78	0.00
12	**Payments for**			
(a)	Bonuses and incentives	213.00	Bonus – guaranteed minimum and production bonus 213 hrs @ 1.00	213.00
(b)	Overtime	131.45	Non-productive overtime 27.5 hrs @ 4.78	131.45
			Annual Wage (A)	1,362.59
		incl. in 11	National Insurance Employers Contribution @ 10% of (A)	136.26*
		incl. in 11	Training Allowance or Industrial Training Levy, e.g. CITB Training Levy 0.50% of PAYE (A)	6.81*
(c)	Working in special circumstances	0.00	WRA Schedule 2 – Working in adverse conditions, e.g. Stone Cleaning, Tunnels, Sewer Work, Working at Height	0.00
(d)	Special allowances			
(e)	Absence due to sickness and holidays	94.92	Holiday Credit 4 wks @ 23.73	94.92
		27.25	Sick Pay Allowance @ 2% of (A) above	27.25
			Paid Total & Allowances (B)	1,627.83
(f)	Severance related to work on this contract	24.42	Allowance for severance pay 1.5% of (B)	24.42
13	**Payments in relation to people for**			
(a)	Travelling to and from the Working Areas	0.00	WR.5 Travel Allowances	0.00
(b)	Subsistence and lodging	508.48	WR.15 Subsistence (where applicable) 4 weeks × 7 nights × £18.16 per night	508.48
(c)	Relocation			0.00
(d)	Medical examinations			0.00
(e)	Passport and visas			0.00
(f)	Travel insurance			0.00
(g)	Items (a) to (f) for a spouse or dependants			0.00
(h)	Protective clothing	8.13	Protective Clothing 0.50% of (B)	8.13
(j)	Meeting the requirements of the law	32.56	Employers Liability and Public Liability Insurance 2% of (B)	32.56
(k)	Superannuation and life insurance	0.00	Industry Pension Scheme	0.00
(l)	Death benefit	3.85	WR.21 Benefit Schemes (Death Benefit Stamp) say	3.85
(m)	Occupational accident benefits			
(n)	Medical aid	33.37	Health Insurance say	33.37
	Total Annual Cost = £	2,238.64	**Total Cost for Period 1 =** £	2,238.64
		incl. in fee percentage	Safety officer's time, QA Policy/inspection and all other costs and overheads, say 2.433% Note: These items are included in the calculation of labour costs using the Working Rule Agreement but are not a Component of People Costs in the ECC	54.47
	Total Annual Cost of General Operative = £	2,238.64	**Total Cost of General Operative for Period 1 =** £	2,293.11
	Total Hours Worked = £	213.00	**Total Hours Worked in Period 1 =** £	213.00
	Cost Per Hour = £	10.51	**Cost Per Hour =** £	10.77

Table A2.2. Example schedule of people rates from a quotations manual

The following are the agreed rates for use on compensation events during the period 1 to 30 June 2005.

Staff	Grade/level	Hourly rate (£)
Project Director	A	50.00
Agent	B	35.00
Site Foreman	C	30.00
QS	D	25.00
Engineer	E1	25.00
Engineer	E2	23.00
Engineer	E3	15.00
Planner	P	30.00
Buyer	B	20.00

Labour	Grade/level	Hourly rate (£)
Ganger	S1	8.00
Bricklayer	S2	10.00
Labourer	S3	*7.00
Painter	S4	9.00
Foreman	S6	12.00
Steel fixer	S7	10.00
Crane operator	S8	8.00
Banksman	S9	7.00

*Note: Rates used for forecast compensation events need to take into consideration future wages and material

covered by this percentage includes:

(a)   offices and drawing offices,
(b)   laboratories,
(c)   workshops,
(d)   stores and compounds,
(e)   labour camps,
(f)   cabins,
(g)   catering,
(h)   medical facilities and first aid,
(j)   recreation,
(k)   sanitation,
(l)   security,
(m)   copying,
(n)   telephone, telex, fax, radio and CCTV,
(o)   surveying and setting out,
(p)   computing,
(q)   hand tools and hand-held powered tools.

If the Contractor has more than one Working Area he will need to sum up the cost of these items (see Table A2.3).

Table A2.3. Allowances within Tendered Total of the prices for the *Contractors* overheads deemed covered by the percentages for Working Area overheads – multiple Sites

List of items	Working Areas			
	A	B	C	Sum
(a) Offices and drawing offices	10,000	9,000	1,000	20,000
(b) Laboratories	1,000	900	—	1,900
(c) Workshops	5,000	—	—	5,000
(d) Stores and compounds	2,000	—	—	2,000
(e) Labour camps	—	—	—	—
(f) Cabins	2,000	2,000	100	4,100
(g) Catering	2,000	—	—	2,000
(h) Medical facilities and first aid	1,000	—	—	1,000
(j) Recreation	—	—	—	—
(k) Sanitation	500	500	—	1,000
(l) Security	750	750	—	1,500
(m) Copying	500	500	—	1,000
(n) Telephone, telex, fax, radio and CCTV	500	500	—	1,000
(o) Surveying and setting out	750	750	250	1,750
(p) Computing	2,000	—	—	2,000
(q) Hand tools and hand-held powered tools	2,000	—	—	2,000
Totals =	**30,000**	**14,900**	**1,350**	**£46,250**

Contract value   =   £750,000

Contract breakdown

Labour (people)   £400,000
Plant   £150,000
Materials   £150,000
Overheads and profit   £50,000
                              £750,000

Express the cost of the Working Area overheads as a percentage of people costs

Note: Total from Table A2.3 above.

$$\frac{\text{Cost of Working Area overheads}}{\text{People costs}} = \frac{46,250}{400,000} \times 100$$

$$= 11.56\%$$

Working Areas overheads say = **12%**

The *Contractor* will insert this figure into Contract Data part two at the time of tender.

It can be seen from the above calculations that the percentage derived of 12% is an average of the three Working Areas. If the majority of compensation events occur within Working Area A then the *Contractor* will not recover his true Working Area overhead for this area. Conversely, if all the compensation events occur in Working Area C then he will make a recovery well over the average.

It is clear therefore that the *Contractor* at the time of tender must make a judgement as to what figure to insert in Contract Data part two. Alternatively, it may be that he might want to suggest the insertion of different percentages for each of the three areas so that they are applied to compensation events which arise in each of the separate areas.

In relation to the quotation example contained in this appendix it is assumed that the 12% Working Area overhead percentage will cover the *Contractor*'s on-site costs. There may of course be times when this may not be the case. In such circumstances the *Contractor* may incur additional costs which are not fully recovered and therefore he may wish to raise this issue with the *Project Manager*.

A2.3.4 Example calculation for percentage for Equipment depreciation and maintenance

For Equipment:

- owned by the *Contractor*,
- purchased by the *Contractor* under a hire purchase or lease agreement,
- hired by the *Contractor* from the *Contractor*'s parent company or another part of a group with the same parent company.

The ECC does not provide for the Actual Cost of internally hired equipment to be an inter-company charge, which is difficult to judge as being fair and reasonable and which could be open to abuse. The ECC introduces instead a surrogate 'hire rate' based on a 'depreciation charge'. An example calculation of an amount for depreciation and maintenance for an item of equipment is as follows:

Dumper truck – calculation of amount for depreciation and maintenance charge

$$\frac{\text{Actual purchase price or first cost paid by current owner}}{\text{working life in weeks (assume available 50 weeks per year remaining at time of purchase)}} \times \frac{\text{number of weeks the Equipment will be in the Working Area}}{}$$

$$\frac{\text{Purchase price £10,000}}{\text{working life}(5\,\text{yrs} \times 50\,\text{wks})} \times \frac{\text{number of weeks the Equipment}}{\text{will be in the Working Area}} = 1\,\text{wk}$$

$$\frac{£10,000}{250} \times 1\,\text{wk} = £40/\text{wk Depreciation and maintenance charge}$$

add

The amount for depreciation and maintenance is calculated by multiplying the depreciation and maintenance charge by the time required in connection with the compensation event and then increasing the product by percentage for equipment depreciation and maintenance stated in Contract Data part two.

Percentage for equipment depreciation and maintenance £40 + 25% = £50/wk (taken from Contract Data part two).

A part week is measured in half days and is expressed as one-twelfth of a week. Therefore 2 days = 2 days $\times \frac{2}{12} = \frac{4}{12} \times £50/\text{wk} = £16.67$.

Half days are charged as one-twelfth of a week.

In the Contract Date part two the *Contractor* is required to insert:

Percentage for equipment depreciation and maintenance (other than special items).

Percentage for depreciation and maintenance for special items of equipment.

The *Contractor* will have to set up two schedules: one for general equipment and another for special items.

An example schedule of Equipment depreciation and maintenance percentages for general equipment is included on page 98 of the ECC2 Guidance Notes.

A2.3.5 Calculation of the percentage for manufacture and fabrication overheads

The following is a simple calculation for the percentage for manufacture and fabrication overheads. This is discussed in more detail in Chapter 2.

Turnover of Fabrication Shop	£1,000,000 p.a.
Labour element of turnover	£500,000 p.a.
Overhead	£100,000 p.a.

Percentage for manufacture and fabrication overheads

$$= \frac{£100,000}{£500,000} \times 100/1 = 20\%$$

A2.3.6 Calculation of the percentage for design overheads

The following is a simple calculation for the percentage for design overheads. This is discussed in more detail in Chapter 2.

Design Office turnover	£2,000,000 p.a.
Labour element of turnover	£1,500,000 p.a.
Overheads	£450,000 p.a.

Percentage for design overheads

$$= \frac{£450,000}{£1,500,000} = 30\%$$

A2.3.7 *Contractor*'s risk

The contract allows in clause 63.5 that the:

'Assessment of the effect of a compensation event includes cost and time risk allowances for matters which have a **significant chance of occurring** and are at the **Contractor's risk** under this contract.'

It should be remembered that the *Contractor* carries all risks except those specifically taken by the *Employer* in the Contract.

The key phrases here are **matters which have a 'significant chance of occurring'** and are at the '**Contractor's risk**'.

The conceptual idea is that the *Contractor* includes in quotations for compensation events for the 'risks' he carries under the Contract in the same way as when he is tendering for the work.

The first exercise for the *Contractor* to undertake is to identify those risks carried by him under the Contract that have a significant chance of impacting the work that is the subtext of the compensation event, including those transferred in new or amended contract conditions. Option Z can be used to introduce additional compensation event clauses for say boundary conditions and there is an entry available in Contract Data part one for the *Employer* to insert additional compensation events, for example suicides/endangered species/eco-warriors.

It therefore may be prudent for the *Contractor* or even the *Employer* at an earlier stage to identify risks carried by the *Contractor*. It is suggested that such a list or pro-forma could be suggested/included in the Works Information so that it is clear from the outset how the *Contractor*'s cost and time risk allowances can be included and in what format they should be submitted with each quotation. An example of a time risk assessment schedule is given in Table A2.4.

In the example given in this appendix there may be no similar items in the original tender therefore the rule should be to include for risks which have **a significant chance of occurring**.

It should be noted that where a *Project Manager* makes his own assessment he should be making allowances for clause 63.5. In this way it is visible how and what has been included in the quotation. It would be prudent to call for this information at the time when the *Contractor* submits his tender.

Risk management should become part of the assessment of a compensation event. Therefore if the *Contractor* can demonstrate that, for example, the ditch referred to has a significant chance of flooding then the *Contractor* should be allowed to make allowance for this risk.

It is **not** the ECC's intention that a blanket percentage is added to each compensation event as has been the temptation on some contracts; risk for each compensation event should be considered for each event. *Contractors* sometimes produce sheets of paper with all sorts of risks equating to a blanket percentage add-on to all compensation events, for example 25%. This is blatantly incorrect and is a dangerous tactic for the *Contractor*, since it means that he is not considering the risk issues properly on each compensation event, which should be of concern to both Parties and is a key principle of the ECC.

Examples of risk *Contractor*'s items are:

• wages increases,
• material increases,

Table A2.4. Sample list of risk events that may need to be considered by the *Contractor* when preparing quotations

Contract title: Spring Field		Contract No: 2003/23		Quotation No: 41 – New Footbridge		
Item No.	Description	Probability (significance low/medium/ high)	How to include (e.g. in people rates, etc.)	Assessment details/ assumptions	Impact assessment time cost	Mitigation details time cost
People						
1	Wage increases	New labour rates as of 1 July 2006	Included in rates	Not applicable	None	Not applicable
2	Labour availability	Low	Not applicable	Not applicable	Not applicable	Not applicable
3	Subcontractor's availability	Low	Not applicable	Not applicable	Not applicable	Not applicable
4	Industrial relations	Low	Not applicable	Not applicable	Not applicable	Not applicable
5	Attendance on Subcontractors (welfare facilities)					
Equipment						
6	Equipment (constructional plant) increases	New rates as of 1 May 2006	Included in rates	Not applicable	None	Not applicable
7	Equipment breakdown/maintenance	Low	Allowances made in output rates	Not applicable	Not applicable	Not applicable
8	Attendance on Subcontractors (Equipment, e.g. scaffold, cranes, etc.)	Low	Allowances made in output rates	Not applicable	Not applicable	Not applicable
Plant and Materials						
9	Plant and Materials availability (shortages/ long lead-in times), delivery delays, etc.	High	Shortage of rebar for foundations	Built into programme for the works	Not applicable	Buffer time built into programme
Manufacture and Fabrication						
10	Manufacture and fabrication delays					
Design						
11	Design liability (increases in design liability) PI insurance	Low	Design liability and PI already covered in main contract	Not applicable	Not applicable	Not applicable
12	Equipment design and temporary works	Low	Not applicable	Not applicable	Not applicable	Not applicable
13	Permanent design	Low	Not applicable	Not applicable	Not applicable	Not applicable
Workmanship/quality						
14	Workmanship/defective work/quality – setting out, etc.	Medium	Allowance made in output rates	Not applicable	Not applicable	Not applicable
15	Subcontractor's performance	Low	Not applicable	Not applicable	Not applicable	Not applicable
Method of working/constraints, etc.						
16	Method of working	Medium	Method of working may require adjacent road closure			
17	Access restrictions	Low	Not applicable	Not applicable	Not applicable	Not applicable
18	Limitations of working space	Low	Not applicable	Not applicable	Not applicable	Not applicable
19	Existing overhead and underground services	Medium	Not applicable	Not applicable	Not applicable	Not applicable
20	Excesses in insurances	Low	Not applicable	Not applicable	Not applicable	Not applicable
21	Security of site (eco-warriors)	Low	Not applicable	Not applicable	Not applicable	Not applicable
22	Impact on future work (e.g. other sections of work/other packages, etc.)	Low	Not applicable	Not applicable	Not applicable	Not applicable
23	Output rates/productivity	Low	Not applicable	Not applicable	Not applicable	Not applicable

Table A2.4. *Continued*

Contract title: Spring Field		Contract No: 2003/23		Quotation No: 41 – New Footbridge	

Item No.	Description	Probability (significance low/medium/ high)	How to include (e.g. in people rates, etc.)	Assessment details/ assumptions	Impact assessment time cost	Mitigation details time cost
24	Health and safety					

Special safety requirements

Employer's risks in contract

25	Weather conditions	Low	If arises will be a compensation event	Not applicable	Not applicable	Not applicable
26	Nature of ground	Low	If arises will be a compensation event	Not applicable	Not applicable	Not applicable
27	Working around other Contractors	Low	If arises will be a compensation event	Not applicable	Not applicable	Not applicable

Changes in the law (secondary Option T)

28	Secondary Option T; if applicable Employer takes the risk for changes in the law (e.g. landfill tax, employment law flexible hours, etc.)	Low	Secondary Option T is included in the contract. If arises it will be a compensation event	Not applicable	Not applicable	Not applicable

Unforeseen risks

29	Foot-and-mouth disease	Low	Not clear in the contract who has this risk?			

- winter working (productivity outputs, etc.),
- equipment hire rate increases,
- change in charges,
- defective work,
- maintenance time for constructional plant.

In some instance the *Employer* reallocates risks such as:

- late flights,
- road closures,
- weather,
- unforeseen ground conditions.

Care also needs to be taken to ensure that allowances are not duplicated, for example allowance made in output rates in the programme and further allowances made in the rates and prices.

Table A2.4 gives an example of what a time risk assessment sheet may look like. This example is by no means meant to be comprehensive. However, it does show how carefully both the *Contractor* and *Employer* should consider risks associated with each compensation event.

A2.3.8 Subcontractors   Table A2.5 shows an example of a Subcontractor's quotation. The example quotation in section A2.2 above includes for electrical works undertaken by Spring Electrics in relation to the new footbridge. It should be noted that the tendering will be for the Subcontractor to submit his quotation in the form of a lump sum. It will be up to the *Contractor* to require the Subcontractor to break the lump sum down to put into his own quotation as shown in section A2.2.

Table A2.5. Example of Subcontractor's quotation

CONTRACT: SPRING FIELD		
QUOTATION FOR COMPENSATION EVENT **(Full Schedule of Cost Components)**		
To: Virtual Contracting Limited	No: 25	
From: Spring Electrics	Sheet: 1	
Brief Description of Works: Electrics to new footbridge	Date: 25 June 2005	
ACTIVITY NO./NOS: **G100**	DELAY TO PLANNED COMPLETION: **0 Days**	SECTION OF WORKS AFFECTED: New Section **3A**

1 PEOPLE

Activity F700 – Electric Lighting to Footbridge

> Note: The *Contactor* needs to take care in the percentage he quotes for Working Areas overheads, as he may not be able to pass through all of the Subcontractor's costs.

	No.	Days	Total days	× hrs	Total hrs	Rate		
Foreman	1	2	2	10	20	20.00	400.00	
Electrician	4	2	8	10	80	15.00	1,200.00	
Trainee electrician	1	2	2	10	20	7.00	140.00	1,740.00

Percentage for Working Areas overheads (Contract Data part two) 50% — 870.00

> Note: The *Contactor* should note the difference between his own and the Subcontractor's Working Areas overheads percentage.

PEOPLE TOTAL CARRIED TO SUMMARY =		£2,610.00

2 EQUIPMENT

Percentage adjustment for listed Equipment (Contract Data part two) ....%

EQUIPMENT TOTAL CARRIED TO SUMMARY =		0.00

3 PLANT AND MATERIALS

Lights	20 No.	@	£100.00	2,000.00	
Cabling	180 m	@	£10.00	1,800.00	3,800.00

PLANT AND MATERIALS TOTAL CARRIED TO SUMMARY		£3,800.00

4 CHARGES

CHARGES TOTAL CARRIED TO SUMMARY =		0.00

5 MANUFACTURE AND FABRICATION

Percentage for manufacturing and fabrication overheads (Contract Data part two) ....%

MANUFACTURE AND FABRICATION TOTAL CARRIED TO SUMMARY =		0.00

6 DESIGN

Percentage for design overheads (Contract Data part two) ....%

DESIGN TOTAL CARRIED TO SUMMARY =		0.00

7 INSURANCE

Deduct from cost:
The cost of events which this contract requires the *Contractor* to insure
and
Other costs paid by the insurer

INSURANCE TOTAL CARRIED TO SUMMARY =		0.00

8 RISK

RISK TOTAL CARRIED TO SUMMARY =		0.00

Table A2.5. *Continued*

<table>
<tr><td colspan="3" align="center">**CONTRACT: SPRING FIELD**</td></tr>
<tr><td colspan="3" align="center">**QUOTATION FOR COMPENSATION EVENT**
(Full Schedule of Cost Components)</td></tr>
<tr><td colspan="2">To: Virtual Contracting Limited</td><td>No: 25</td></tr>
<tr><td colspan="2">From: Spring Electrics</td><td>Sheet: 1</td></tr>
<tr><td colspan="2">Brief Description of Works: Electrics to new footbridge</td><td>Date: 25 June 2005</td></tr>
<tr><td>ACTIVITY NO./NOS:
G100</td><td>DELAY TO PLANNED COMPLETION:
0 Days</td><td>SECTION OF WORKS AFFECTED:
New Section **3A**</td></tr>
</table>

SUMMARY	£
1. PEOPLE	2,610.00
2. EQUIPMENT	0.00
3. PLANT AND MATERIALS	3,800.00
4. CHARGES	0.00
5. MANUFACTURE AND FABRICATION	0.00
6. DESIGN	0.00
7. INSURANCE	0.00
8. RISK	0.00
TOTAL =	£6,410.00
9. FEE *Fee percentage* (Subcontractors Contract Data part two) 20....%	£1,282.00
TOTAL =	**£7,692.00**

Note potential difference between Subcontractor's and *Contractor's fee percentage.*

Distribution:	Original to:	Project Manager	
	Copies to:	Contract File	Supervisor

Note: In this priced-based example the definition of Actual Cost A11.2(28) and B11.2(28) is the cost in the Schedule of Cost Components whether work is subcontracted or not.

Clause A63.10 and B63.10 state the assessment of a compensation event which is or includes subcontracted work has the *Contractor's fee percentage* added to Actual Cost but fees paid or to be paid by the *Contractor* to the Subcontractor are not added.

Note: If the example were a cost based Options C, D, E or F. Then the definition of Actual Cost C11.2.27, D11.2(27), E11.2(27), F11.2(26) includes payments due to Subcontractors for work which is subcontracted.

A2.3.9 Activity Schedule Table A2.6 shows how the quotation for this compensation event may translate into new activities.

A2.3.10 Some reminders
- Cost and time effects of change are valued and adjusted collectively.
- The emphasis is on pre-pricing/pre-assessment of compensation events using forecasts Actual Cost (as defined in the Schedule of Cost Component) of work not yet done.
- Tendered rates and prices are not generally used to assess change (in main Options B and D *bill of quantities* rates can be used by agreement).
- Costs of work already done based on Actual Cost.
- Assessments not revisited or adjusted when based on assumptions which are later corrected.
- Cost based on Actual Cost as defined in the Schedule of Cost Component.
- Time based on entitlement not needs.
- Assessment to include *Contractor's* cost and time risk allowances.

Table A2.6. Example activity schedule build-up

Contract Spring Field
Activity Schedule – New Footbridge

Build-up to activity totals

Activity No.	Description	Total	People	Working Areas Overhead 12% (allocated across activities)	Equipment	Plant and Materials	Charges	Manufacture and fabrication outside of the Working Areas	Design outside of the Working Areas	Insurances	Risk
F100	Design	8,791.20	885.00	106.20					7,800.00		
F200	Fabricate footbridge	21,140.00		0.00		12,500.00		8,640.00			
F250	Set up site	4,174.66	2,361.60	283.39	879.67		650.00				
F260	Enabling work	3,480.61	1,731.20	207.74	1,541.67						
F270	Footbridge foundations	7,362.75	2,496.50	299.58	166.67	4,400.00					
F300	Assemble footbridge on site	6,697.79	5,751.00	690.12	256.67						
F400	Brick wingwalls	2,278.72	1,680.40	201.65	256.67	140.00					
F500	Paint bridge	1,394.00	1,200.00	144.00	50.00						
F600	Clear site	2,402.47	1,651.00	198.12	553.35						
F700	Electric lighting	5,748.80	1,740.00	208.80		3,800.00					
				0.00							
Subtotals		63,471.00	19,496.70	2,339.60	3,704.70	20,840.00	650.00	8,640.00	7,800.00	0.00	0.00
			Check for people	21,836.30							
Fee percentage 10%		6,347.10									
Total =		**£69,818.10**									

Table A2.7. Example extract of the people element of a quotation using the Shorter SCC

PEOPLE						
Activity F250 – Set up site (5 days)			Note: Hourly rates will be lower than in the full SCC.			
	No.	*Hrs*	*Total hrs*	*Rate*		
Foreman	1	24	24	12.00	288.00	
Labourers	4	40	160	10.00	1,600.00	
Ganger	1	40	40	7.00	380.00	2,168.60
Activity F300, etc.						10,000.00
Note: See Table A2.8 below for build-up for percentage for people overheads.			**Total for people**		= £	12,168.60
			Percentage for people overheads + 31%			3,650.40
			TOTAL FOR PEOPLE		= £	15,818.40

A2.4 Shorter Schedule of Cost Components – example quotation

The contract recognises that the production of a quotation based on the full Schedule of Cost Components may not always be necessary and in main Options A, B, C, D and E in clause 63.11, if the *Project Manager* and *Contractor* agree, the *Contractor* assesses a compensation event using the Shorter Schedule of Cost Components.

1. People

The cost component for people is identical to the full Schedule of Cost Components but the components in 12 and 13 have been shortened to 12 (a) to (d) and 13 (a) and (b). This shortfall in people costs goes in to component Charges 4 (a) overhead payments for people including payroll burdens.

Table A2.7 shows an extract of the people element of a quotation using the Shorter SCC.

2. Equipment

- Amounts for Equipment in the published list identified in Contract Data part two adjusted by the percentage adjustment listed in Contract Data part two. The published list for example will be the Civil Engineering Contractors Association Daywork Schedule, or RICS Daywork Schedule, etc.

The entry in Contract Data part two is as follows:

Note: An adjustment is required on Equipment listed in published lists, e.g. CECA Daywork, because the rates already include for an element of overheads and profit in the listed rates which in ECC is included in the Fee.

- The published list of Equipment is the last edition of the list published by ...... CECA ....
- The percentage for adjustment for listed Equipments is .... −30% ......
- The rates for other Equipment are

Equipment	Size or capacity	Rate
....	....	....

3. Plant and Materials

The same as the full Schedule of Cost Components.

4. Charges

Similar to Charges in the full Schedule of Cost Components and the Working Areas overhead percentage in the full SCC. The FSCC clauses 41 to 43 are included in clause 4 of the SSCC and therefore form part of the people percentage.

In the SSCC the costs identified separately in items 41, 42 and 43 are also included in a percentage applied to people costs and this is known as the percentage for people overheads.

Table A2.8. Example build-up for people percentage for Shorter Schedule of Cost Components

Item		Description	Non-time related	Rate	Per	Duration	Total
					Time-related charge		
(a) Overhead payments for people including payroll burdens							
	Shortfall in people components 12 and 13	£708.11 shortfall per year per direct employee – site has 30 people: £708.11/52 weeks = £13.61 per wk per employee × 50 = £680.50 per week		680.50	per employee	30 wks	20,415.00
(b) Payments to utilities for the provision and use in the Working Areas of				Note: See Appendix 3 Table A3.2 for calculation of people costs.			
Provision							
	Water	connection charge	250.00				
		site installation	200.00				
		disconnection	100.00				
	Gas	connection charge	0.00				
		site installation	200.00				
		disconnection	0.00				
	Electricity	connection charge	250.00				
		site installation	200.00				
		disconnection	100.00				
Use of							
	Water	water supply charge	0.00	20.00	per wk	30 wks	600.00
	Gas	gas supply charge	0.00	0.00	per wk	0 mths	0.00
	Electricity	electricity supply charge	0.00	200.00	per wk	30 wks	6,000.00
(c) Payments to public authorities, utilities and other properly constituted authorities of charges which they are authorised to make in respect of the works							
(d) Payments for							
	Financing charges (excluding charges compensated for by interest paid in accordance with this contract)						
	Buying or leasing land	temporary lease of land for compound	2,500.00	—	—	—	—
	Compensation for loss of crops or buildings	compensation for loss of crops to Farmer Jones	1,000.00	—	—	—	—
	Royalties	royalties for use of patented paint for bridge	100.00	—	—	—	—
	Inspection certificates	building regulation inspections	250.00	—	—	—	—
	Rent of premises in the Working Areas	rent for site offices	—	10.00	per wk	30 wks	300.00
	Charges for access to the Working Areas	charge for access via wayleave to rear of site	500.00	—	—	—	—
	Facilities for visits to the Working Area by Others	visitors' PPE (personal protection equipment)	500.00	—	—	—	—
		furniture rental	—	10.00	per wk	30 wks	300.00
		TV and video rental	—	5.00	per wk	30 wks	150.00
	Specialist services		—	—	—	—	—
Payments for							
	Accommodation	10 office staff × 8 m² = 80 m²		120.00	per wk	30 wks	3,600.00
		canteen		40.00	per wk	30 wks	1,200.00
		washroom		25.00	per wk	30 wks	750.00
		staff toilets		30.00	per wk	30 wks	900.00
		site toilets		30.00	per wk	30 wks	900.00
		welfare facilities		100.00	per wk	30 wks	3,000.00
	Equipment	office equipment	100.00	—	—	—	—
		testing equipment rental	—	10.00	per wk	30 wks	300.00
		fire-fighting equipment rental	—	10.00	per wk	30 wks	300.00
		camera rental	—	2.50	per wk	30 wks	75.00
		sign boards and traffic signs	500.00	—	—	—	—
	Supplies and services for offices	General Office expenditure – tea, milk, sugar, washing-up liquid, mugs, stationery, stamps, film, etc.	100.00	10.00	per wk	30 wks	300.00
		office cleaner (part-time)	—	25.00	per wk	30 wks	750.00
		furniture and equipment rental	—	35.00	per wk	30 wks	1,050.00
		c/f	£6,850.00				£40,890.00

c#### Table A2.8. *Continued*

Item	Description		Non-time related	Time-related charge			
				Rate	Per	Duration	Total
		c/f	£6,850.00				£40,890.00
	furniture and office equipment – purchase price less residual value		500.00	—	—	—	—
Drawing office	general expenditure		—	—	—	—	—
Laboratories	general expenditure		—	20.00	per wk	30 wks	600.00
Workshops	general expenditure		—	20.00	per wk	30 wks	600.00
Stores and compounds	stores		—	20.00	per wk	30 wks	600.00
	general expenditure		—	20.00	per wk	30 wks	600.00
Labour camps — Note: Particularly relevant on international projects.			—	—	—	—	—
Cabins	general expenditure		—	—	—	—	—

Note: Assumed that this will include *Contractor*'s welfare facilities which are not specifically mentioned in component 41.

Item	Description	Non-time related	Rate	Per	Duration	Total
Catering	catering services provided by Well Feed Limited	—	250.00	per wk	30 wks	7,500.00
Medical facilities and first aid	medical equipment and supplies	500.00	—	—	—	—
Recreation	five-a-side football pitch — Note: Particularly relevant on international projects.					
Sanitation	cess pit cleaning	—	25.00	per wk	30 wks	750.00
Security	site security guard	—	100.00	per wk	30 wks	3,000.00
	security hut and barriers	—	60.00	per wk	30 wks	1,800.00
	site hoarding and lighting – set-up and removal	2,000.00	—	—	—	—
Copying	photocopier monthly hire charge	—	10.00	per wk	30 wks	300.00
Telephone	installation and disconnection	200.00	—	—	—	—
	monthly telephone bills	—	20.00	per wk	30 wks	600.00
Fax	installation and disconnection of dedicated phone line	200.00	—	—	—	—
	monthly telephone line bills	—	10.00	per wk	30 wks	300.00
Radio	provision of 10 No. hand-held radios	500.00	—	—	—	—
CCTV	installation of CCTV cameras to site perimeter 10 No. and control system	1,000.00	—	—	—	—
	removal of CCTV cameras on completion	300.00	—	—	—	—
	provision of CCTV tapes	200.00	—	—	—	—
Surveying and setting out	survey equipment rental	—	30.00	per wk	30 wks	900.00
	purchase cost pegs, paint, profiles, etc.	500.00	—	—	—	—
Computing	provision of 2 No. office computers	1,000.00				
	purchase of planning software	300.00				
	installation of ADSL line	100.00				
	rental for ADSL line	—	5.00	per wk	30 wks	150.00
	printers 2	500.00	—	—	—	—
	printer ink cartridges	—	5.00	per wk	30 wks	150.00
Hand tools and hand-held power tools + A52	small tools, say 1.5% of labour costs (assume labour costs £250,000) say	3,750.00	—	—	—	—
Subtotals	**Non-time-related costs to summary = £**	**18,400.00**	**Time-related costs to summary = £**			**58,740.00**

Summary	£
Non-time-related	£ 18,400.00
Time-related	£ 58,740.00
Total cost for component 41	**£ £77,140.00**

Contract breakdown

Labour	250,000.00
Materials	150,000.00
Equipment (constructional plant)	150,000.00
Profit	50,000.00
Total contract value	**£600,000.00**

Calculation for percentage for people overheads

$$\frac{77,140.00}{250,000.00} \times \frac{1.00}{100.00}$$

Percentage for people overheads = **30.86%**

say = **31%**

112   © copyright nec 2005   www.neccontract.com

Table A2.9. Example quotation for the Shorter Schedule of Cost Components

CONTRACT: SPRING FIELD								

QUOTATION FOR COMPENSATION EVENT   **SHORTER**
SHORTER SCHEDULE OF COST COMPONENTS

To: Project Manager	No: 41
From: Virtual Contracting Limited	Sheet: 1
Brief Description of Works: Provision of Footbridge to Spring Dyke Due to Road Realignment	Date: 1 July 2005

ACTIVITY NO./NOS: **A500**	DELAY TO PLANNED COMPLETION: **1 Day**	SECTION OF WORKS AFFECTED: **3A**

1. PEOPLE

Activity 500 – kerbing to roads and footpaths

	No.	Days	Total days	Hrs	Total hrs	Rate		
Foreman	1	2	2	10	20	15.00	300.00	
Labourer	2	2	4	10	40	10.00	400.00	

Note: See example Contract Data part two – data provided by the *Contractor*: Data for the Shorter Schedule of Cost Components and example people % build-up in Table A2.8.

| | Subtotal | 700.00 |
| Percentage for people percentage +31% | | 217.00 |

PEOPLE TOTAL CARRIED TO SUMMARY   £917.00

2. EQUIPMENT

Notes: Rates for Equipment taken from published list stated in Contract Data part two, e.g. CECA Daywork Schedule.

Activity 500 – kerbing to roads and footpaths

	No.	Days	Total days	Hrs	Total hrs	Rate		
Dumper	1	2	2	10	20	20.00	400.00	
Lorry	1	2	2	10	20	20.00	400.00	

Note: See example Contract Data part two: Data for the Shorter Schedule of Cost Components.

| | Subtotal | 800.00 |
| Equipment adjustment −30% | | 240.00 |

The rates for other listed Equipment

Note: See example Contract Data part two: Data for the Shorter Schedule of Cost Components.

EQUIPMENT TOTAL CARRIED TO SUMMARY =   £560.00

3. PLANT AND MATERIALS

Activity 500 – kerbing to roads and footpaths

	No.	Rate						
Standard kerbs	20	20.00					400.00	
Drop kerbs	4	50.00					200.00	
								600.00

PLANT AND MATERIALS TOTAL CARRIED TO SUMMARY =   £600.00

4. CHARGES (included in people percentage added to item 1 People above)   £ 00.00

5. MANUFACTURE AND FABRICATION OUTSIDE OF THE WORKING AREAS

None
Employee costs   £

Note: See Contract Data part two data provided by the *Contractor* – Data for Schedule of Cost Components.

| | Subtotal | |
| Manufacture and fabrication overhead +20% | | |

TOTAL CARRIED TO SUMMARY =   £ 00.00

6. DESIGN OUTSIDE OF THE WORKING AREAS		
None		
Employee costs £		
Note: see Contract Data part two data provided by the *Contractor* – Data for Schedule of Cost Components. Subtotal		
Design overhead +30%		
DESIGN OUTSIDE OF THE WORKING AREAS TOTAL CARRIED TO SUMMARY =		£ 00.00
7. INSURANCES		
None		
INSURANCES TOTAL CARRIED TO SUMMARY =		£ 00.00
8. CONTRACTOR'S TIME/RISK ALLOWANCES — Note: See example time/risk schedule in Table A2.4.		
None		
CONTRACTOR'S TIME/RISK ALLOWANCES TOTAL CARRIED TO SUMMARY =		£ 00.00

SUMMARY	£
1. PEOPLE	917.00
2. EQUIPMENT	560.00
3. PLANT AND MATERIALS	600.00
4. CHARGES	0.00
5. MANUFACTURE AND FABRICATION	0.00
6. DESIGN	0.00
7. INSURANCES	0.00
8. CONTRACTOR'S TIME/RISK ALLOWANCES	0.00
Subtotal =	£2,077.00
9. FEE Fee percentage 10% — Note: See example Contract Data part two – data provided by the *Contractor* in section 2 above.	207.70
Grand Total =	**£2,284.70**

As a general rule the percentage for people overheads should be greater than the Working Area overhead percentage because it includes more items.

An example for the calculation for percentage for people overheads is shown in Table A2.8.

5. Manufacture and fabrication
The same as the full Schedule of Cost Components, see section A2.3.5 above.

6. Design
The same as the full Schedule of Cost Components, see section A2.3.6 above.

7. Insurance
The same as the full Schedule of Cost Components.

8. *Contractor*'s Risk
The same as the full Schedule of Cost Components, see section A2.3.7 above.

Section B – ECC3 only

Example quotations for compensation events

(Based on the full Schedule of Cost Components (FSCC) and Shorter Schedule of Cost Components (SSCC))

B2.1 Introduction

In this Section B we reproduce for ECC3 the example of a quotation based on the full Schedule of Cost Components for a hypothetical compensation event on the project named Spring Field given in Section A for ECC2.

The compensation event is for the provision of a new footbridge over the existing Spring Dyke following the realignment of Spring Road. For the purposes of this example it is assumed that the new footbridge will be a new *section* of *works* (created by a supplemental agreement) to the existing contract for Spring Field.

We assume for the purposes of this example that the contract has been let on an ECC Option C Target Contract with Activity Schedule. It should be noted that in ECC3 the FSCC is only used for main Options C, D and E; it is not used with main Options A and B.

This example sets out a format for the presentation of the quotation and includes build-ups, supporting notes and comments on some of the issues surrounding the preparation of quotations for ECC3.

Figure B2.1 shows a sectional view of the proposed new footbridge. A programme for the *works* has been prepared and is shown in Fig. B2.2.

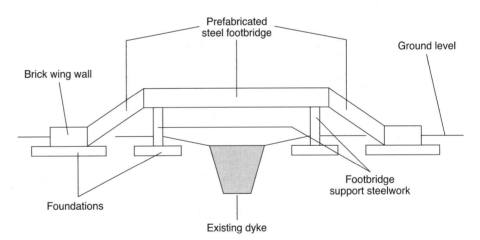

Fig. B2.1. Proposed new footbridge over Spring Dyke

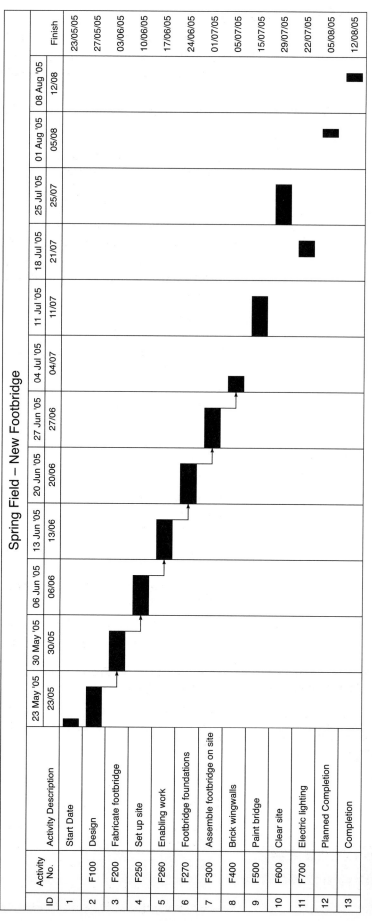

nec Managing Change

Spring Field – New Footbridge

ID	Activity No.	Activity Description	23 May '05 23/05	30 May '05 30/05	06 Jun '05 06/06	13 Jun '05 13/06	20 Jun '05 20/06	27 Jun '05 27/06	04 Jul '05 04/07	11 Jul '05 11/07	18 Jul '05 21/07	25 Jul '05 25/07	01 Aug '05 05/08	08 Aug '05 12/08	Finish
1		Start Date													23/05/05
2	F100	Design													27/05/05
3	F200	Fabricate footbridge													03/06/05
4	F250	Set up site													10/06/05
5	F260	Enabling work													17/06/05
6	F270	Footbridge foundations													24/06/05
7	F300	Assemble footbridge on site													01/07/05
8	F400	Brick wingwalls													05/07/05
9	F500	Paint bridge													15/07/05
10	F600	Clear site													29/07/05
11	F700	Electric lighting													22/07/05
12		Planned Completion													05/08/05
13		Completion													12/08/05

Fig. B2.2. Programme for the new footbridge over Spring Dyke

116 © copyright nec 2005   www.neccontract.com

B2.2 Contract Data – example

The following is an example of a quotation for the new footbridge.

The Contract Data part two extracted from the documents which are part of the contract used to produce this example quotation is shown below.

Contract Data part two – Data provided by the *Contractor*

Statements given in all contracts

• The *Contractor* is

Name	Virtual Contracting Limited
Address	Virtual House
	Virtual Lane
	Virtual City

> Note: In ECC3 the Fee comprises a *direct* and *subcontracted fee percentage* – clause 11.2(8).

• The *direct fee percentage* is 10%.

• The *subcontracted fee percentage* is 5%.

• The *working areas* are the Site and the area indicated on drawing FYK001 as lay-down and prefabrication facilities.

• The key people are:

(1) Name	Joe Bloggs
Job	Site Agent
Responsibilities	....
Qualifications	....
Experience	....

(2) Name	John Public
Job	QS
Responsibilities	....
Qualifications	....
Experience	....

> Note: Matters identified by the *Employer* for the Risk Register.
>
> The Risk Register has been introduced as part of the endorsement from the OGC (Office of Government Commerce).

• The following matters will be included in the Risk Register
  • Flooding
  • Unchartered services

• The Works Information for the *Contractor*'s design is in the document entitled 'Contractor's Proposal'.

• The programme identified in the Contract Data is in the document entitled 'Contractor's Programme'.

Option A

• The *activity schedule* is in the document entitled 'Activity Schedule'.

• The tendered total of the Prices is £1,843,000.

Data for Schedule of Cost Components

• The listed items of Equipment purchased for work in this contract, with an on-cost charge are

> Note: This replaces the maintenance and depreciation charge in ECC2.
>
> See item 23 in FSCC.

Equipment	time-related charge	per time period
Adjustable height restriction framework for vehicles	£100.00	per week
....	....	....
....	....	....

• The rates for special Equipment are

> Note: The Working Areas overhead in ECC3 excludes accommodation.
>
> See example build-up in section B2.6.3.

Equipment	size/capacity	rate
bridge jack	2000 ton	£50 per wk
....	....	....
....	....	....

• The percentage for Working Areas overheads is 9.50%

- The hourly rates for Defined Cost of manufacture or fabrication outside the Working Areas are

category of employee	Hourly rate
Foreman	£20
Fabricators	£20

Note: See example build-up in section B2.6.5.

- The percentage for manufacture or fabrication overheads is 20%.

Data for both Schedules of Cost Components

- The hourly rates for Defined Cost of design outside the Working Areas are:

category of employee	hourly rate
Draughtsman	£30

Note: See item B2.6.6 for build-up.

- The percentage for design overheads is 30%.

- The categories of design employees whose travelling expenses to and from the Working Areas are included as a cost of design of the *works* and Equipment done outside of the Working Areas are

  None.

Data for the Shorter Schedule of Cost Components

- The percentage for people overheads is 23%.

- The published list of Equipment is the last edition of the list published by CECA.

- The percentage for adjustment for Equipment in the published list is −30%.

- The rates for other Equipment are:

Equipment	size or capacity	rate
....	....	....
....	....	....

B2.3 Defined Cost

In ECC3 Defined Cost for the full Schedule of Cost Components consists of two components:

(1)   Defined Cost of subcontracted work:
- to which is added the *Contractor*'s *subcontracted fee percentage* as stated in Contract Data part two

and

(2)   Defined Cost of other work (work undertaken directly by the *Contractor*):
- to which is added the *Contractor*'s *direct fee percentage* as stated in Contract Data part two

B2.4 Direct and subcontracted fee percentages

In ECC3 the work undertaken directly by the *Contractor* and the work which he subcontracts form two sides of the Defined Cost as shown in Fig. B2.3. However, in ECC2 the *Contractor* included the amount of payments to the Subcontractors in Actual Cost[218] and then applied the *fee percentage*[219] stated by him in Contract Data part two.

In ECC3 the *Contractor* declares a *direct fee percentage* and a separate *subcontracted fee percentage* to be applied to the amount of subcontracted work.

The *direct fee percentage* will be much like the build-up for the *fee percentage*[220] stated in ECC2 and will cover such items as:

(1)   Head office charges and overheads (should not duplicate the overheads recovered in Contract Data part two for manufacture and fabrication overheads and design overheads):
- loss of money insurance – loss of money due to theft,

---

[218]ECC2 only.
[219]ECC2 only.
[220]ECC2 only.

Fig. B2.3. Composition of Defined Cost

- fidelity guarantee insurance – act of frauds or dishonesty,
- fire insurance – permanent premise and contents.

(2)   Components not covered in the Schedule of Cost Components include, for example:

- insurance premiums,
  - professional indemnity insurance (*contractor*-designed work),
  - *Employer*'s liability insurance,
  - vehicle insurance,
  - public liability insurance,
  - all risks insurance – loss or damage to permanent and/or temporary *works* and also covers Equipment and Plant and Materials,[221]
    - corporation tax,
- advertising and recruitment costs,
- sureties and guarantees,
- indirect payments to staff on overseas contracts.

(3)   *Contractor*'s profit.

The *subcontracted fee percentage* will cover:

(1)   *Contractor*'s profit and
(2)   *Contractor*'s overheads in relation to the management of subcontracts.

It is assumed that attendance on subcontractors (e.g. use of welfare facilities, use of *Contractor*'s scaffolding, tower crane) will be recovered via the Schedule of Cost Components.

---

[221]Constructional plant.

B2.5 Full schedule of cost components – example quotation

We will now look at an example quotation for a compensation event for ECC3 followed by an example of a Subcontractor's quotation.

B2.5.1 Defined cost of other work (direct work)

CONTRACT: SPRING FIELD

QUOTATION FOR COMPENSATION EVENT

To: Project Manager	Note: Effect on overall planned Completion should be stated here. In this particular example it is assumed that this work can be undertaken with the main *works*.	No: 41
From: Virtual Contracting Limited		Sheet: 1

Brief Description of Works: Provision of Footbridge to Spring Dyke Due to Road Realignment		Date: 1 July 2005

ACTIVITY NO./NOS: **F100 to F700**	DELAY TO PLANNED COMPLETION: **1 Day**	SECTION OF WORKS AFFECTED: **3A**	AFFECT ON KEY DATE: **Area 1–5 Days**

1 PEOPLE

Note: The Activity Numbers should relate to the *activity schedule* and the Accepted Programme.

Note: As well as the Prices and the Completion Date and any changes to Key Dates need to be notified. See clause B2.6.2.

Activity F250 – Set up site (5 days)

	No.	Hrs	Total Hrs	Rate		
Foreman	1	24	24	15.00	360.00	
Labourers	4	40	160	10.51	1,681.60	
Ganger	1	40	40	8.00	320.00	2,361.60

Activity F260 – Enabling Work (5 days)

Note: See supporting notes section B2.6 and sample calculation for calculating the cost of people B2.6.1.

	No.	Hrs	Total Hrs	Rate		
Foreman	1	16	16	15.00	240.00	
Labourers	3	40	120	10.51	1,261.20	1,501.20

Activity F270 – Footbridge Foundations (5 days)

	No.	Hrs	Total Hrs	Rate		
Foreman	1	40	40	15.00	600.00	
Labourers	3	50	150	10.51	1,576.50	
Ganger	1	40	40	8.00	320.00	2,496.50

Activity F300 – Assemble Footbridge on site (5 days)

	No.	Hrs	Total Hrs	Rate		
Foreman	1	50	50	15.00	750.00	
Ganger	1	50	50	8.00	400.00	
Steel fixers	4	50	200	12.00	2,400.00	
Crane operator	1	50	50	12.00	600.00	
Banksman	1	50	50	11.00	550.00	
Labourers	2	50	100	10.51	1,051.00	5,751.00

PEOPLE c/f						£12,110.30

CONTRACT: SPRING FIELD								
QUOTATION FOR COMPENSATION EVENT								

To: Project Manager	No: 41
From: Virtual Contracting Limited	Sheet: 2
Brief Description of Works: Provision of Footbridge to Spring Dyke Due to Road Realignment	Date: 1 July 2005

ACTIVITY NO./NOS: **F100 to F700**	DELAY TO PLANNED COMPLETION: **1 Day**	SECTION OF WORKS AFFECTED: **3A**	AFFECT ON KEY DATE: **Area 1–5 Days**

					PEOPLE b/f			£12,110.30

Activity F400 – Brick Wingwalls (2 days)

	No.	Days	Total days	×Hrs	Total Hrs	Rate		
Foreman	1	2	2	10	20	15.00	300.00	
Bricklayers	4	2	8	10	80	12.00	960.00	
Labourer	2	2	4	10	40	10.51	420.40	1,680.40

Activity F500 – Paint Bridge (5 days)

	No.	Days	Total days	×Hrs	Total Hrs	Rate		
Painters	2	5	10	10	100	12.00	1,200.00	1,200.00

Activity F600 – Clear Site (5 days)

	No.	Days	Total days	×Hrs	Total Hrs	Rate		
Foreman	1	5	5	8	40	15.00	600.00	
Labourer	2	5	10	10	100	10.51	1,051.00	1,651.00

Activity No. F100 Site Staff Costs – Preparation of Quotation

Note that for Options C, D and E the preparation of quotations is an allowable cost.

	Hrs	Rate		
QS	10	25.00	250.00	
Engineer E1	8	25.00	200.00	
Buyer	7	20.00	140.00	
Site Agent	5	35.00	175.00	
Planner	4	30.00	120.00	885.00

PEOPLE c/f		£17,526.70

CONTRACT: SPRING FIELD			
QUOTATION FOR COMPENSATION EVENT			
To: Project Manager		No: 41	
From: Virtual Contracting Limited		Sheet: 3	
Brief Description of Works: Provision of Footbridge to Spring Dyke Due to Road Realignment		Date: 1 July 2005	

ACTIVITY NO./NOS: **F100 to F700**	DELAY TO PLANNED COMPLETION: **1 Day**	SECTION OF WORKS AFFECTED: **3A**	AFFECT ON KEY DATE: **Area 1–5 Days**
		PEOPLE b/f	£17,526.70

Activity F260 – Enabling Work
(5 days)

- People who are directly employed by the *Contractor* and whose normal place of work is not the Working Area but are working in the Working Areas – clause 1

Supervision of the erection of temporary works by Head Office – temporary works supervisor.

Team Leader   1 day   80.00

> Note: 11 paid according to time worked while in the Working Areas.

- People who are not directly employed by the *Contractor* but are paid for by him according to the time worked while they are in the Working Area – component 14

> Note: Component 14 amounts paid by the *Contractor*.

Inspection of the erected temporary works by Independent Third Party   1 day   150.00   230.00

> See sample calculation in attached supporting notes section B2.6.3. Consideration may also need to be given to whether this percentage is appropriate given that this is a new section of *works*. Includes an absorption of Subcontractor's Working Areas overheads as shown in example subcontractor's quotation.

Subtotal		£17,756.70
Working Area overhead +9.5%		1,686.89
PEOPLE TOTAL CARRIED TO SUMMARY =		£19,443.59

CONTRACT: SPRING FIELD		
QUOTATION FOR COMPENSATION EVENT		

To: Project Manager	No: 41
From: Virtual Contracting Limited	Sheet: 4
Brief Description of Works: Provision of Footbridge to Spring Dyke Due to Road Realignment	Date: 1 July 2005

ACTIVITY NO./NOS: **F100 to F700**	DELAY TO PLANNED COMPLETION: **1 Day**	SECTION OF WORKS AFFECTED: **3A**	AFFECT ON KEY DATE: **Area 1–5 Days**

2 EQUIPMENT

Activity F250 – Set up Site

> See detailed calculation notes in section B2.6.4 of attached supporting notes.

2 Equipment (includes cost of accommodation but excluding Equipment cost covered for Working Area overheads)

Contractor's offices

Section office – 1 No. at 10 m^2	6 wks	@	£30/wk	180.00	
Contractor's site huts					
Store	6 wks	@	£20/wk	120.00	
Site toilet	6 wks	@	£25/wk	150.00	450.00

Activity F250 – Set up Site (5 days)

21 – Hired/Rented Equipment
(at hire rate or rental rate multiplied by the time for which the Equipment is required)

Dumper	5 days	@	£50/wk	50.00	
Lorry	5 days	@	£100/day	500.00	
Shovel			say	10.00	
Hand-saw			say	20.00	580.00

> Note: See component item 44(j); these hand-held tools are included in the Working Area overhead percentage.

Activity F260 – Enabling work
(5 days)

Dumper	5 days	@	£50/wk	50.00	
Hired Equipment					
Lorry	5 days	@	£100/day	500.00	
Excavator	5 days	@	£200/day*	1000.00	1,550.00

Activity F270 – Footbridge Foundations
(5 days)

> Note: Ensure that the Equipment rate excludes the people cost.

Dumper	5 days	@	£50/wk	50.00	
Hired Equipment					
Concrete mixer	5 days	@	£20/day	100.00	
Wheelbarrow	5 days	@	£5/day	25.00	175.00

EQUIPMENT c/f		£2,755.00

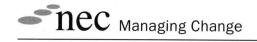

CONTRACT: SPRING FIELD		
QUOTATION FOR COMPENSATION EVENT		

To: Project Manager	No: 41
From: Virtual Contracting Limited	Sheet: 5
Brief Description of Works: Provision of Footbridge to Spring Dyke Due to Road Realignment	Date: 1 July 2005

ACTIVITY NO./NOS: **F100 to F700**	DELAY TO PLANNED COMPLETION: **1 Day**	SECTION OF WORKS AFFECTED: **3A**	AFFECT ON KEY DATE: **Area 1–5 Days**
		EQUIPMENT b/f	£2,755.00

Activity F300 – Assemble Footbridge on Site
(2 days)

Dumper	2 days	@	£10/day	20.00	
Lorry	1 day	@	£100/day	100.00	
Setting out equipment			say	40.00	160.00

22 Payments for Equipment which is not listed in the Contract Data but is owned, purchased or hired by the *Contractor*

> Note: At open market rates, multiplied by the time for which the Equipment is required.

Hired Equipment					
Crane (inc. driver, delivery and removal from site)	2 days	@	£50/day	100.00	100.00

> Note: Inclusion of driver with crane. If inserted here you will not recover in the Working Area overhead percentage as well.

Activity F400 – Brick Wingwalls
(2 days)

Dumper	2 days	@	£10/day	20.00	
Hired Equipment					
Lorry	2 days	@	£100/day	200.00	
Concrete mixer	1 day	@	£40/day	40.00	260.00

Activity F500 – Paint Bridge
(5 days)

> Note: These types of items need to be listed in Contract Data part two.

Hired Equipment					
Trestles	5 days	@	£10/day	50.00	50.00

Activity F600 – Clear Site
(5 days)

Dumper	7 days	@	£10/day	70.00	
Hired Equipment					
Lorry	5 days	@	£100/day	500.00	570.00

EQUIPMENT c/f		£3,895.00

CONTRACT: SPRING FIELD			
QUOTATION FOR COMPENSATION EVENT			
To: Project Manager		No: 41	
From: Virtual Contracting Limited		Sheet: 6	
Brief Description of Works: Provision of Footbridge to Spring Dyke Due to Road Realignment		Date: 1 July 2005	
ACTIVITY NO./NOS: **F100 to F700**	DELAY TO PLANNED COMPLETION: **1 Day**	SECTION OF WORKS AFFECTED: **3A**	AFFECT ON KEY DATE: **Area 1–5 Days**
EQUIPMENT b/f			£3,895.00

Activity F250 – Set up site						
23 Payments for Equipment purchased for work in this contract listed with a time-related charge						
• Adjustable height restriction framework for vehicles	@	£100/wk	4 wks		£400.00	£400.00
Activity 300 – Assemble footbridge						
24 Payments for special Equipment listed in the Contract Data						
• Bridge Jacks 4 No.	@	£50/wk	4 wks		£800.00	
Additional item of special Equipment						
• Bridge deck lifting eyes	@	£10/wk	4 wks		£40.00	£840.00
Activity F250 – Set up site						
25 Payments for the purchase of Equipment which is consumed						
• Sacrificial framework 10 sheets	@	20			200.00	
• Fuel for Generator 10 litres	@	80p/litre			8.00	208.00
Activity 300 – Assemble footbridge						
26 Unless included in the hire or rental rates, payments for						
• Transporting crane to and from site					100.00	
• Erecting and dismantling crane					100.00	
• Modifying jib of crane to lift bridge sections					500.00	700.00
27 Payments for purchase of materials used to construct or fabricate Equipment						
Materials for modifying jib of crane to lift bridge sections						
• Steel sections/RSAs					250.00	
• Lifting eye and chains					200.00	450.00
28 Unless included in the hire rates, the cost of operatives is included in the cost of people						

Note: This replaces the maintenance and depreciation charge in ECC2.

Note: If the *Project Manager* agrees, an additional item of special Equipment may be assessed as if it had been listed in the Contract Data.

Note: New item in ECC3 to cover these items when it was not clear in ECC2.

Note: Inclusion of driver with crane above. If the cost of the driver is included with the Equipment the Working Area overhead percentage will not be recovered on that person.

EQUIPMENT TOTAL CARRIED TO SUMMARY =		**£6,493.00**

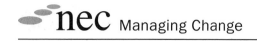

CONTRACT: SPRING FIELD			
QUOTATION FOR COMPENSATION EVENT			

To: Project Manager	No: 41		
From: Virtual Contracting Limited	Sheet: 7		
Brief Description of Works: Provision of Footbridge to Spring Dyke Due to Road Realignment	Date: 1 July 2005		

ACTIVITY NO./NOS: **F100 to F700**	DELAY TO PLANNED COMPLETION: **1 Day**	SECTION OF WORKS AFFECTED: **3A**	AFFECT ON KEY DATE: **Area 1–5 Days**

3   PLANT AND MATERIALS

Activity F200 – Fabricate Footbridge
31 Purchasing Plant and Materials
Materials for Footbridge

• Durasteel	100 m²	@	£50	5,000.00	
• RSA 45 × 45 mm	100 m	@	£5	500.00	
• Black bolts	500 No.	@	£2	1,000.00	
• Stainless steel handrails	60 m	@	£100	6,000.00	12,500.00

Activity F270 – Footbridge Foundations

Concrete	80 m³	@	£50	4,000.00	
Formwork	20 sheets	@	£20	400.00	4,400.00

Activity F400 – Brick wing walls

Bricks	2000 No.	@	£0.05p	100.00	
• Providing and removing packaging					
Providing storage boxes for the delivery of bridge bolts			£10.00	10.00	
(Returned pallet)			(−£10)	(−10.00)	
Disposal of polystyrene and cellophane wrapping around special bricks			50.00	50.00	
• Samples and tests					
Brick sample			£50	50.00	
Paint sample board			£50	50.00	
32 Cost is credited with payments received for disposal of Plant and Materials					
Surplus brick – restocked by stockist			Less		50.00
			£200.00	(−200.00)	

Note: Reflects growing environmental requirements.

PLANT AND MATERIALS TOTAL CARRIED TO SUMMARY =	**£16,950.00**

CONTRACT: SPRING FIELD			
QUOTATION FOR COMPENSATION EVENT			
To: Project Manager		No: 41	
From: Virtual Contracting Limited		Sheet: 8	
Brief Description of Works: Provision of Footbridge to Spring Dyke Due to Road Realignment		Date: 1 July 2005	
ACTIVITY NO./NOS: **F100 to F700**	DELAY TO PLANNED COMPLETION: **1 Day**	SECTION OF WORKS AFFECTED: **3A**	AFFECT ON KEY DATE: **Area 1–5 Days**

4   CHARGES

Activity F250

41 Payments for provision and use in Working Areas of

1 Payment for temporary connection charges by Water Authority	50.00	
2 Payment for temporary connection and disconnection of electrical supply to LEB	50.00	100.00

42 Payments to public authorities

1 Local Authority inspection charge	50.00	50.00

43 Payments for (a) to (i), e.g. 43(c)

1 Payment to Mr Jones for access to the Working Area and loss of crops	500.00	500.00

44 A charge for overhead costs incurred within the Working Areas

> Note: Items 44(a) to (j) are a list of charges for the provision and use of equipment, supplies and services (but excludes accommodation), within the Working Areas. These items are included in the percentage for Working Area overheads added to item 1. People as stated by the *Contractor* in Contract Data part two.

CHARGES TOTAL CARRIED TO SUMMARY =   **£650.00**

CONTRACT: SPRING FIELD			
QUOTATION FOR COMPENSATION EVENT			
To: Project Manager		No: 41	
From: Virtual Contracting Limited		Sheet: 9	
Brief Description of Works: Provision of Footbridge to Spring Dyke Due to Road Realignment		Date: 1 July 2005	
ACTIVITY NO./NOS: **F100 to F700**	DELAY TO PLANNED COMPLETION: **1 Day**	SECTION OF WORKS AFFECTED: **3A**	AFFECT ON KEY DATE: **Area 1–5 Days**

5 MANUFACTURE AND FABRICATION

5 *The following components of cost of manufacture and fabrication of Plant and Materials, which are*

- *Wholly or partly designed specifically for the works and*
- *Manufactured or fabricated outside the Working Areas*

Activity F200 – Fabrication of Footbridge

51 The total of the hours worked by employees multiplied by the hourly rates stated in the Contract Data for the categories of employees listed

Employee Costs

Foreman	5 days × 8 hrs	40	@	£20	800.00	
Fabricators, 8 men	5 days × 8 hrs	320	@	£20	6,400.00	7,200.00
Subtotal						7,200.00

52 An amount for overheads calculated by multiplying this total by the percentage for manufacturing and fabrication overheads stated in the Contract Data

Percentage for manufacturing of fabrication overheads stated in Contract Data part two +20%   1,440.00

Note: See section B2.2, example of Contract Data part two.

MANUFACTURE AND FABRICATION TOTAL CARRIED TO SUMMARY =	**£8,640.00**

CONTRACT: SPRING FIELD			
QUOTATION FOR COMPENSATION EVENT			
To: Project Manager		No: 41	
From: Virtual Contracting Limited		Sheet: 10	
Brief Description of Works: Provision of Footbridge to Spring Dyke Due to Road Realignment		Date: 1 July 2005	
ACTIVITY NO./NOS: **F100 to F700**	DELAY TO PLANNED COMPLETION: **1 Day**	SECTION OF WORKS AFFECTED: **3A**	AFFECT ON KEY DATE: **Area 1–5 Days**

6 DESIGN		
Activity F100 Design		
61 The total of the hours worked by employees multiplied by the hourly rates stated in the Contract Data for the categories of employees listed.		
(A) *Employee Cost*		
Draughtsman, 4 men × 10 hrs per day × 5 days = 200 hrs @ £30	6,000.00	
62 An amount for overheads calculated by multiplying this total by the percentage for design overheads stated in the Contract Data		
(B) Percentage for design overheads taken from Contract Data part two +30% Note: See section B2.2, example of Contract Data part two.	1,800.00	
63 The cost of travel to and from the Working Areas for the categories of design employees in the Contract Data		
(C) Travel costs (in Contract Data part two included in employee hourly rate)	N/A	7,800.00
DESIGN TOTAL CARRIED TO SUMMARY =		**£7,800.00**
7 INSURANCE		
Deduct from cost:		
• The cost of events which this contract requires the *Contractor* to insure	N/A	
and		
• Other costs paid by the insurer	N/A	
INSURANCE TOTAL CARRIED TO SUMMARY =		N/A

CONTRACT: SPRING FIELD			
QUOTATION FOR COMPENSATION EVENT			
To: Project Manager		No: 41	
From: Virtual Contracting Limited		Sheet: 9	
Brief Description of Works: Provision of Footbridge to Spring Dyke Due to Road Realignment		Date: 1 July 2005	
ACTIVITY NO./NOS: **F100 to F700**	DELAY TO PLANNED COMPLETION: **1 Day**	SECTION OF WORKS AFFECTED: **3A**	AFFECT ON KEY DATE: **Area 1–5 Days**
SUMMARY 1. PEOPLE			£19,443.59
2. EQUIPMENT			£6,493.00
3. PLANT AND MATERIALS			£16,950.00
4. CHARGES			£650.00
5. MANUFACTURE AND FABRICATION			£8,640.00
6. DESIGN			£7,800.00
7. INSURANCE			N/A
		Subtotal	£59,976.59
8. RISK ALLOWANCES			£0.00
		Subtotal (Defined Cost of other work – clause 11.2(8))	**£59,976.59**
9. FEE Note: See example Contract Data part two in section B2.2. *Direct Fee Percentage 10%*			£5,997.66
TOTAL DEFINED COST OF OTHER WORK			**£65,974.25**
10. Subcontracted Work 1. Spring Electrics (see attached build-up in B5.2 below) 2. etc.			£7,692.00
11. FEE *Subcontracted fee percentage 5%*			£384.60
TOTAL DEFINED COST OF SUBCONTRACTED WORK = Note: See example Contract Data part two in section B2.2.			**£8,076.60**
TOTAL DEFINED COST OTHER WORK			£65,974.25
TOTAL DEFINED COST SUBCONTRACTED WORK[222]			£8,076.60
TOTAL DEFINED COST OF OTHER WORK SUBCONTRACTED WORK =			**£74,050.85**

[222]See Table B2.1 below.

B2.5.2 Defined Cost Subcontractor's work
Table B2.1 shows an example of the Spring Electrics quotation for their *works* in relation to the new footbridge. It should be noted that it is highly likely that the subcontractor will submit his quotation in the form of a lump sum. It will be up to the *Contractor* to break the lump sum down to put into his own quotation.

Table B2.1. Example of Subcontractor's quotation

CONTRACT: SPRING FIELD

QUOTATION FOR COMPENSATION EVENT (Full Schedule of Cost Components)

To: Virtual Contracting Limited	No: 25
From: Spring Electrics	Sheet: 1
Brief Description of Works: Electrics to new footbridge	Date: 25 June 2005

ACTIVITY NO./NOS: G100	DELAY TO PLANNED COMPLETION: **0 Days**	SECTION OF WORKS AFFECTED: **3A**	AFFECT ON KEY DATE: **Area 1–5 Days**

1 PEOPLE

Activity F700 – Electric Lighting to Footbridge

	No.	Days	Total days	× hrs	Total hrs	Rate		
Foreman	1	2	2	10	20	20.00	400.00	
Electrician	4	2	8	10	80	15.00	1,200.00	
Trainee electrician	1	2	2	10	20	7.00	140.00	1,740.00
Percentage for Working Areas overheads (Subcontractor's Contract Data part two) 50.....%								870.00
PEOPLE TOTAL CARRIED TO SUMMARY =								**£2,610.00**

2 EQUIPMENT

Percentage adjustment for listed Equipment (Contract Data part two) .....%	
EQUIPMENT TOTAL CARRIED TO SUMMARY =	£ 0.00

3 PLANT AND MATERIALS

Lights	20 No.	@	£100.00	2,000.00	
Cabling	180 m	@	£10.00	1,800.00	3,800.00
PLANT AND MATERIALS TOTAL CARRIED TO SUMMARY =					**£3,800.00**

4 CHARGES

CHARGES TOTAL CARRIED TO SUMMARY =	£ 0.00

5 MANUFACTURE AND FABRICATION

Percentage for manufacturing and fabrication overheads (Contract Data part two) .....%	
MANUFACTURE AND FABRICATION TOTAL CARRIED TO SUMMARY =	£ 0.00

6 DESIGN

Percentage for design overheads (Contract Data part two) .....%	
DESIGN TOTAL CARRIED TO SUMMARY =	£ 0.00

7 INSURANCE

Deduct from cost:
The cost of events which this contract requires the *Contractor* to insure
and
Other costs paid by the insurer

INSURANCE TOTAL CARRIED TO SUMMARY =	£ 0.00

8 RISK

RISK TOTAL CARRIED TO SUMMARY =	£ 0.00

Table B2.1. *Continued*

CONTRACT: SPRING FIELD			
QUOTATION FOR COMPENSATION EVENT (Full Schedule of Cost Components)			
To: Virtual Contracting Limited		No: 25	
From: Spring Electrics		Sheet: 1	
Brief Description of Works: Electrics to new footbridge		Date: 25 June 2005	
ACTIVITY NO./NOS: **G100**	DELAY TO PLANNED COMPLETION: **0 Days**	SECTION OF WORKS AFFECTED: **3A**	AFFECT ON KEY DATE: **Area 1–5 Days**

SUMMARY	£
1. PEOPLE	2,610.00
2. EQUIPMENT	0.00
3. PLANT AND MATERIALS	3,800.00
4. CHARGES	0.00
5. MANUFACTURE AND FABRICATION	0.00
6. DESIGN	0.00
7. INSURANCE	0.00
8. RISK	0.00
TOTAL DIRECT WORK =	£6,410.00
9. FEE *Direct fee percentage* (see Contract Data part two) 20....%	£1,282.00
TOTAL DEFINED COST FOR OTHER WORK =	**£7,692.00**
TOTAL SUBCONTRACTED WORK =	
10. None	0.00
11. FEE *Subcontracted fee percentage* (see Contract Data part two) 5%	0.00
TOTAL DEFINED COST FOR SUBCONTRACTED WORK =	**£0.00**
TOTAL DEFINED COST OTHER WORK	£7,692.00
TOTAL DEFINED COST SUBCONTRACTED WORK	£0.00
TOTAL DEFINED COST OF OTHER WORK SUBCONTRACTED WORK =	**£7,692.00**

Distribution:	Original to:	*Project Manager*	
	Copies to:	Contract File	*Supervisor*

B2.6 Supporting notes

The following supporting notes seek to amplify and support the example quotation given in section B2.2 above.

1	People – calculation of people (labour) costs
2	Example schedule of people rates from a quotations manual
3	Calculating the Working Areas overhead percentage
4	Example calculation for percentage for Equipment purchased for work included in the contract
5	Calculation of the percentage for manufacture and fabrication overheads
6	Calculation of the percentage for design overheads
7	*Contractor*'s risk allowances
8	Activity Schedule
9	Some reminders

B2.6.1 People – calculation of people (labour) costs

It is based upon:[223]

- the Defined Cost (as defined by the Schedule of Cost Components) of the work already done,
- the forecast Defined Cost of the work not yet done and
- the resulting Fee.

The Fee[224] is defined as: the sum of the amounts calculated by applying the *subcontracted fee percentage* to the Defined Cost of subcontracted work and the *direct fee percentage* to the Defined Cost of other work.

It is important to note that tender rates and prices are not used to assess change and in all instances the cost for the different grades of people involved will be based on:

- a payroll printout showing the required information,
- proof of other payments such as lodging allowances,
- other documentary evidence.

Table B2.2 shows a typical example of a contractor's payroll printout and a build-up for the cost of people based on the components in the full Schedule of Cost Components.

In theory this exercise based on the *Contractor*'s accounts and records is needed for each and every category of people on each and every quotation for a compensation event. This principle is adequate where compensation events are few and far between but on larger projects it may not be so practical.

Some employers and contractors have agreed on larger projects to do this exercise once a month or every quarter to establish a list of agreed rates to use for quotations. Some have developed what are called quotation manuals which are included at the time of tender to establish the first people costs and other costs for use to assess compensation events. This document is then reviewed every month and a set of project-wide rates for the month or period ahead. This is particularly useful on large, multi-location projects which have large teams of people on the project.

Although this is not strictly ECC it is a practical way of providing consistency of approach across a project and reduces the need for too many people to have to get involved in establishing the Defined Cost of People and reduces the fears of the *Contractor* in having to adopt an open-book approach on sensitive commercial information.

It also makes the audit of compensation events a great deal more simple.

[223]Clause 63.1.
[224]Clause 11.2(8).

Table B2.2. Example of a *Contractor*'s payroll

Payroll Build-up Based on Full Schedule of Cost Components			Traditional calculation of hourly rates for labour based on the Working Rule Agreement		
General Operative Mr X for Period 1: 4-week period from 1 to 30 June 2005			General Operative Mr X for Period 1: 4-week period from 1 to 30 June 2005		
11	**Wages and Salary** *(Figure made up of Basic Rate, Additional Payments for skill, National Insurance and Training Levy Allowance from traditional build-up opposite)* [Items marked with an asterisk]	1,161.21	Basic Rate of Pay (Classification – General Operative, Skill Rate 1, 2, 3, 4, Craft Rate) 213 hrs @ 4.78		1,018.14*
		0.00	Additional Payment for Skilled Work WRA (Schedule 1 – Classification i, ii, iii) 0 hrs @ 4.78		0.00*
12	**Payments for**				
(a)	Bonuses and incentives	213.00	Bonus – guaranteed minimum and production bonus 213 hrs @ 1.00		213.00
(b)	Overtime	131.45	Non-productive overtime 27.5 hrs @ 4.78		131.45
			Annual Wage (A)		1,362.59
		incl. in 11	National Insurance Employers Contribution @ 10% of (A)		136.26
		incl. in 11	Training Allowance or Industrial Training Levy, e.g. CITB Training Levy 0.50% of PAYE (A)		6.81
(c)	Working in special circumstances	0.00	WRA Schedule 2 – Working in adverse conditions e.g. Stone Cleaning, Tunnels, Sewer Work, Working at Height		0.00
(d)	Special allowances				
(e)	Absence due to sickness and holidays	94.92	Holiday Credit 4 wks @ 23.73		94.92
		27.25	Sick Pay Allowance @ 2% of (A) above		27.25
			Paid Total & Allowances (B)		1,627.83
(f)	Severance related to work on this contract	24.42	Allowance for severance pay 1.5% of (B)		24.42
13	**Payments in relation to people for**				
(a)	Travel	0.00	WR.5 Travel Allowances		0.00
(b)	Subsistence and lodging	508.48	WR.15 Subsistence (where applicable) 4 weeks × 7 nights × £18.16 per night		508.48
(c)	Relocation				0.00
(d)	Medical examinations				0.00
(e)	Passport and visas		Note: The difference between the £10.51 in the Schedule of Cost Components (SCC) and the £10.77 in the traditional build-up should be included in the Fee.		0.00
(f)	Travel insurance				0.00
(g)	Items (a) to (f) for dependants				0.00
(h)	Protective clothing	8.31	Protective Clothing 0.50% of (B)		8.13
(i)	Meeting the requirements of the law	32.56	Employers Liability and Public Liability Insurance 2% of (B)		32.56
(j)	Pensions and life insurance	0.00	Industry Pension Scheme		0.00
(k)	Death benefit	3.85	WR.21 Benefit Schemes (Death Benefit Stamp) say		3.85
(l)	Occupational accident benefits				
(m)	Medical aid	33.37	Health Insurance say		33.37
(n)	A vehicle	0.00			
(o)	Safety training	0.00			
	Total Annual Cost = £	2,238.64	**Total Cost for Period 1 =** £		2,238.64
		incl in fee percentage	Safety officer's time, QA Policy/inspection and all other costs and overheads, say 2.433% Note: These items are included in the calculation of labour costs using the Working Rule Agreement but are not a Component of People Costs in the ECC		54.47
	Total Annual Cost of General Operative = £	2,238.64	**Total Cost of General Operative for Period 1 =** £		2,293.11
	Total Hours Worked = £	213.00	**Total Hours Worked in Period 1 =** £		213.00
	Cost Per Hour = £	10.51	**Cost Per Hour =** £		10.77

nec Managing Change

Table B2.3. Example schedule of people rates from a quotations manual

The following are the agreed rates for use on compensation events during the period 1 to 30 June 2005.

Staff	Grade/level	Hourly rate (£)
Project Director	A	50.00
Agent	B	35.00
Site Foreman	C	30.00
QS	D	25.00
Engineer	E1	25.00
Engineer	E2	23.00
Engineer	E3	15.00
Planner	P	30.00
Buyer	B	20.00

Labour	Grade/level	Hourly rate (£)
Ganger	S1	8.00
Bricklayer	S2	10.00
Labourer	S3	*7.00
Painter	S4	9.00
Foreman	S6	12.00
Steel fixer	S7	10.00
Crane operator	S8	8.00
Banksman	S9	7.00

*Note: rates used for forecast compensation events need to take into consideration future wages and material

B2.6.2 Example schedule of people rates from a quotations manual

Table B2.3 gives an extract from a quotations manual which shows the agreed hourly rates to be used in the assessment of compensation events during a month or period.

B2.6.3 Calculation for Working Areas overhead percentage

This percentage, added to the cost of people, covers the costs of the *Contractor*'s on-site overheads in his Working Areas.

The *Contractor* at the time of tender inserts in the Contract Data part two his required Working Areas overheads.

Component 44 in ECC3 now excludes the *Contractor*'s accommodation from the Working Areas overhead percentage, which were included in ECC2 44(a) to (f), for example offices and drawing offices, laboratories, workshops, stores and compounds, labour camps, cabins.

The charge includes the provision and use of equipment, supplies and services, but excludes accommodation for:

(a) catering,
(b) medical facilities and first aid,
(c) recreation,
(d) sanitation,
(e) security,
(f) copying,
(g) telephone, telex, fax, radio and CCTV,
(h) surveying and setting out,
(i) computing,
(j) hand tools not powered by compressed air.

Table B2.4. Allowances within Tendered Total of the prices for the *Contractor*'s overheads deemed covered by the percentages for Working Area overheads – multiple sites, ECC3 only

List of items	Working areas			
	A	B	C	Sum
(a) catering	3,000	—	—	3,000
(b) medical facilities and first aid	1,000	—	—	1,000
(c) recreation	—	—	—	—
(d) sanitation	500	500	—	1,000
(e) security	750	750	—	1,500
(f) copying	500	500	—	1,000
(g) telephone, telex, fax, radio and CCTV	500	500	—	1,000
(h) surveying and setting out	750	750	250	1,750
(i) computing	2,000	—	—	2,000
(j) hand tools not powered by compressed air	2,000	—	—	2,000
Totals =	11,000	3,000	250	£14,250

If the *Contractor* has more than one Working Area he will need to sum up the cost of these items (see Table B2.4).

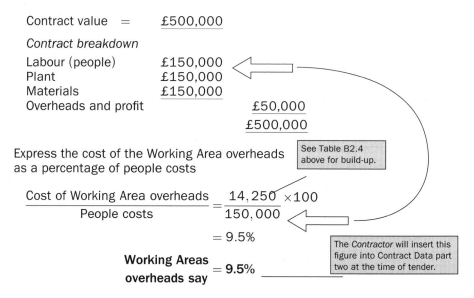

Contract value   =   £500,000

Contract breakdown

Labour (people)	£150,000
Plant	£150,000
Materials	£150,000
Overheads and profit	£50,000
	£500,000

Express the cost of the Working Area overheads as a percentage of people costs

See Table B2.4 above for build-up.

$$\frac{\text{Cost of Working Area overheads}}{\text{People costs}} = \frac{14,250 \times 100}{150,000}$$

$$= 9.5\%$$

Working Areas overheads say $= 9.5\%$

The *Contractor* will insert this figure into Contract Data part two at the time of tender.

It can be seen from the above that the percentage derived of 9.50% is an average of the three Working Areas. If the majority of compensation events occur within Working Area A then the *Contractor* will not recover his true Working Area overhead for this area. Conversely, if all the compensation events occur in Working Area C then he will make a recovery well over the average.

It is clear therefore that the *Contractor* at the time of tender must make a judgement as to what figure to insert in Contract Data part two. Alternatively, it may be that he might want to suggest the insertion of different percentages for each of the three areas so that they are applied to compensation events which arise in each of the separate areas.

In relation to the quotation example contained in this appendix it is assumed that the 9.50% Working Area overhead percentage will cover the *Contractor*'s on-site costs. There may of course be times when this may not be the case. In such circumstances the *Contractor* may incur additional costs which are not fully recovered and therefore he may wish to raise this issue with the *Project Manager*.

Table B2.5. Schedule of Equipment purchased for the project – examples

Item	A – purchase price	B – period required	C – sale price	D – difference between purchase and sale price (A−C)	E – time-related on-cost, see Contract Data part two
Dumper truck	£15,000.00	3 months	Say £13,000.00	£2,000.00	£20 per week for maintenance and repairs
Tunnel boring machine	£150,000.00	12 months	Say £120,000.00	£30,000.00	£500 per month for maintenance and repairs

B2.6.4 Example calculation for Equipment purchased for work included in the contract

ECC3 has dispensed with the maintenance and depreciation charge and replaced it with a more practical and realistic way of looking at Equipment purchased specifically for work on a project. A good example of this may be the purchase of a tunnel boring machine (TBM), which could be new or refurbished, used for 12 months on a project. At the end of the project the TBM can be sold on to others.

23 Payments for Equipment purchased for work included in this contract listed with a time-related on-cost charge, in the Contract Data, of:

- *the change in value over the period for which the Equipment is required and*
- *the time-related on-cost charge stated in the Contract Data for the period for which the Equipment is required.*

An example calculation for cost component 23 for an item of Equipment purchased for the project is given in Table B2.5.

B2.6.5 Calculation of the percentage for manufacture and fabrication overheads

The following is a simple calculation for the percentage for manufacture and fabrication overheads. This is discussed in more detail in Chapter 2.

Turnover of Fabrication Shop	£1,000,000 p.a.
Labour element of turnover	£500,000 p.a.
Overhead	£100,000 p.a.

Percentage for manufacture and fabrication overheads

$$= \frac{£100,000}{£500,000} \times 100/1 = 20\%$$

B2.6.6 Calculation of the percentage for design overheads

The following is a simple calculation for the percentage for design overheads. This is discussed in more detail in Chapter 2.

Design Office turnover	£2,000,000 p.a.
Labour element of turnover	£1,500,000 p.a.
Overheads	£450,000 p.a.

Percentage for design overheads

$$= \frac{£450,000}{£1,500,000} \times 100/1 = 30\%$$

B2.6.7 *Contractor*'s risk allowances

The contract states in clause 63.6 that the

'Assessment of the effect of a compensation event includes risk allowances for cost and time for matters which have a **significant chance of occurring** and are at the *Contractor*'s risk under this contract.'

It should be remembered that the *Contractor* carries all risks except those specifically taken by the *Employer* in the Contract.

The key phrases here are **matters which have 'significant chance of occurring'** and are at the '*Contractor*'s risk'.

The conceptual idea is that the *Contractor* includes in quotations for compensation events for the 'risks' those he carries under the contract in the same way as when he is tendering for the work.

The first exercise for the *Contractor* to undertake is to identify possible risks carried by him under the contract that have a significant chance of impacting the work that is the subject of the compensation event, including those transferred in new or amended contract conditions. Option Z can be used to introduce additional compensation event clauses for say boundary conditions and there is space left in Contract Data part one for the *Employer* to insert additional compensation events, for example suicides/endangered species/eco-warriors.

It therefore may be prudent for the *Contractor* or even the *Employer* at an earlier stage to identify risks carried by the *Contractor*. It is suggested that such a list or pro-forma could be suggested/included in the Works Information so that it is clear from the outset how the *Contractor*'s cost and time risk allowances are to be included and in what format they should be submitted with each quotation. An example of a *Contractor*'s risk allowances schedule is given in Table B2.6.

In the example given in this appendix there may be no similar items in the original tender, therefore the rule should be to include for risks which have **a significant chance of occurring.**

It should be noted that where a *Project Manager* makes his own assessment he should be making allowances for clause 63.6. In this way it is visible how and what has been included in the quotation.

It would be prudent to call for this information at the time when the *Contractor* submits his tender. Risk management should now become part of the assessment of a compensation event.

Therefore if the *Contractor* can demonstrate that, for example, the ditch referred to has a significant chance of flooding, then the *Contractor* should be allowed to make allowance for this risk.

It is **not** the ECC's intention that a blanket percentage is added to each compensation event as has been the temptation on some contracts; risk for each compensation event should be considered on each event. *Contractors* sometimes produce sheets of paper with all sorts of risks equating to a blanket percentage add-on to all compensation events, for example 25%. This is blatantly incorrect and is a dangerous tactic for the *Contractor*, since it means that he is not considering the risk issues properly on each compensation event, which should be of concern to both Parties and is a key principle of the ECC.

Examples of *Contractor*'s risk items are:

- wage increases,
- material increases,
- winter working (productivity outputs, etc.),
- equipment hire rate increases,
- change in charges,
- defective work,
- maintenance time for constructional plant.

In some instance the *Employer* reallocates risks such as:

- late flights,
- road closures,
- weather,
- unforeseen ground conditions.

Care also needs to be taken to ensure that allowances are not duplicated, for example allowance made in output rates in the programme and further allowances made in the rates and prices.

In ECC3 the *Employer* is required to list Contract Data part one item 1 General, the matters to be included in the Risk Register.[225] Likewise the *Contractor* is required to do the same in Contract Data part two.

[225]Clause 11.2(14).

Table B2.6. Sample list of risk events that may need to be considered by the *Contractor* when preparing quotations

Contract title: Spring Field		Contract No: 2003/23		Quotation No: 41 – New Footbridge		
Item No.	Description	Probability (significance low/medium/ high)	How to include (e.g. in people rates, etc.)	Assessment details/ assumptions	Impact assessment/ time, cost	Mitigation details/time, cost
People						
1	Wage increases	New labour rates as of 1 July 2006	Included in rates	Not applicable	None	Not applicable
2	Labour availability	Low	Not applicable	Not applicable	Not applicable	Not applicable
3	Subcontractor's availability	Low	Not applicable	Not applicable	Not applicable	Not applicable
4	Industrial relations	Low	Not applicable	Not applicable	Not applicable	Not applicable
5	Attendance on Subcontractors (welfare facilities)					
Equipment						
6	Equipment (constructional plant) increases	New rates as of 1 May 2006	Included in rates	Not applicable	None	Not applicable
7	Equipment breakdown/maintenance	Low	Allowances made in output rates	Not applicable	Not applicable	Not applicable
8	Attendance on Subcontractors (Equipment, e.g. scaffold, cranes, etc.)	Low	Allowances made in output rates	Not applicable	Not applicable	Not applicable
Plant and Materials						
9	Plant and Materials availability (shortages/ long lead-in times), delivery delays, etc.	High	Shortage of rebar for foundations	Built into programme for the works	Not applicable	Buffer time built into programme
Manufacture and Fabrication						
10	Manufacture and fabrication delays					
Design						
11	Design liability (increases in design liability) PI insurance	Low	Design liability and PI already covered in main contract	Not applicable	Not applicable	Not applicable
12	Equipment design and temporary works	Low	Not applicable	Not applicable	Not applicable	Not applicable
13	Permanent design	Low	Not applicable	Not applicable	Not applicable	Not applicable
Workmanship/quality						
14	Workmanship/defective work/quality – setting out, etc.	Medium	Allowance made in output rates	Not applicable	Not applicable	Not applicable
15	Subcontractor's performance	Low	Not applicable	Not applicable	Not applicable	Not applicable
Method of working/constraints, etc.						
16	Method of working	Medium	Method of working may require adjacent road closure			
17	Access restrictions	Low	Not applicable	Not applicable	Not applicable	Not applicable
18	Limitations of working space	Low	Not applicable	Not applicable	Not applicable	Not applicable
19	Existing overhead and underground services	Medium	Not applicable	Not applicable	Not applicable	Not applicable
20	Excesses in insurances	Low	Not applicable	Not applicable	Not applicable	Not applicable
21	Security of site (eco-warriors)	Low	Not applicable	Not applicable	Not applicable	Not applicable
22	Impact on future work (e.g. other sections of work/other packages, etc.)	Low	Not applicable	Not applicable	Not applicable	Not applicable
23	Output rates/productivity	Low	Not applicable	Not applicable	Not applicable	Not applicable

Table B2.6. *Continued*

		Probability (significance low/medium/ high)	How to include (e.g. in people rates, etc.)	Assessment details/ assumptions	Impact assessment/ time, cost	
Contract title: Spring Field			Contract No: 2003/23			Quotation No: 41 – New Footbridge
Item No.	Description					Mitigation details/time, cost
24	Health and safety					

Special safety requirements

Employer's risks in contract

25	Weather conditions	Low	If arises will be a compensation event	Not applicable	Not applicable	Not applicable
26	Nature of ground	Low	If arises will be a compensation event	Not applicable	Not applicable	Not applicable
27	Working around other Contractors	Low	If arises will be a compensation event	Not applicable	Not applicable	Not applicable

Changes in the law (secondary Option X2)

28	Secondary Option X2; if applicable Employer takes the risk for changes in the law (e.g. landfill tax, employment law flexible hours, etc.)	Low	Secondary Option T is included in the contract. If arises it will be a compensation event	Not applicable	Not applicable	Not applicable

Unforeseen risks

29	Foot-and-mouth disease	Low	Not clear in the contract who has this risk?			

The intent of this Risk Register is to identify from the outset of the contract the potential risks associated with the contract. The risk is described and a description of the actions to be taken to avoid or reduce the risk.

Table B2.6 shows how a *Contractor* could show risk allowances associated with a compensation event. This example is by no means meant to be comprehensive. However, it does show how carefully both the *Contractor* and *Employer* should consider risks associated with each compensation event. As well as identifying the specific risks for an event it may also highlight new risks which should be identified on the contract Risk Register (see Table B2.7).

B2.6.8 Activity Schedule Table B2.8 shows how the quotation for this compensation event may translate into new activities in the build-up to how the Activity Schedule.

Table B2.7. Matters to be added to Risk Register

Contract No: 2005/23		Quotation No: 41 – New Footbridge				
Matters						
Description		Probability (significance low/medium/ high)	How to include (e.g. in people rates, etc.)	Assessment details/ assumptions	Impact assessment/ time, cost	Mitigation details/time, cost
Planning approval for bridge delayed		Low	Not applicable	Approval received by the x of May 05	Delay to project start date	Working closely with *Project Manager* and local authority to gain planning permission. Looking at possibility of pre-assembly off-site.

Table B2.8. Example activity schedule build-up

| Contract Spring Field Activity Schedule – New Footbridge | | | | Build-up to activity totals | | | | | | | |
Activity No.	Description	Total	People	Working Area overhead 9.5% (allocated across activities)	Equipment	Plant and Materials	Charges	Manufacture and fabrication outside of the Working Areas	Design outside of the Working Areas	Insurances	Risk
DIRECT WORK											
F100	Design	8,769.08	885.00	84.08					7,800.00		
F200	Fabricate footbridge	21,140.00		0.00		12,500.00		8,640.00			
F250	Set up site	4,873.95	2,361.60	224.35	1,638.00		650.00				
F260	Enabling work	3,445.66	1,731.20	164.46	1,550.00						
F270	Footbridge foundations	7,308.67	2,496.50	237.17	175.00	4,400.00					
F300	Assemble footbridge on Site	8,547.35	5,751.00	546.35	2,250.00						
F400	Brick wingwalls	2,150.04	1,680.40	159.64	260.00	50.00					
F500	Paint bridge	1,364.00	1,200.00	114.00	50.00						
F600	Clear site	2,377.85	1,651.00	156.85	570.00						
	Subtotal	59,976.59	17,756.70	1,686.89	6,493.00	16,950.00	650.00	8,640.00	7,800.00	0.00	0.00
	Direct fee percentage 10%	5,997.66									
Total Defined Cost for Direct Work = £		**£69,974.25**									

Main Contractor's direct fee percentage, see Contract Data part two.

Check for People

19,443.59

Table B2.8. Continued

Contract Spring Field
Activity Schedule – New Footbridge

Build-up to activity totals

Activity No.	Description	Total	People	Working Area overhead 50% (allocated across activities)	Equipment	Plant and Materials	Charges	Manufacture and fabrication outside of the Working Areas	Design outside of the Working Areas	Insurances	Risk	Subcontractor's direct fee percentage 20%	Subcontractor's subcontracted fee percentage 5%
SUBCONTRACT WORK													
F700	Electric lighting	7692.00	1,740.00	870.00		3,800.00						1.282	
	Subtotal	7692.00											
	Subcontract fee percentage 5%	384.60											
Total Defined Cost for Direct Work = £		**£8,076.60**	1,740.00	870.00	0.00	3,800.00	0.00	0.00	0.00	0.00	0.00	1,282.00	0.00
Total Defined Cost – Direct and Subcontract Work = £		**£74,050.85**	Check for People	2,610.00									

Subcontractor's Working Area overhead % from Contract Dat part two.

Main Contractor's subcontract fee percentage, see Contract Data part two.

These are the Subcontractor's own *direct* and *subcontracted fee* percentages which will be found in his Contract Data part two.

B2.6.9 Some reminders
- Cost and time effects of change are valued and adjusted collectively.
- Emphasis on pre-pricing/pre-assessment of compensation events using forecasts (Defined Cost as defined in the Schedule of Cost Component) of work not yet done.
- Tendered rates and prices are not generally used to assess change (in main Options B and D BQ rates can be used by agreement).
- Costs of work already done based on Defined Cost.
- Assessments not revisited or adjusted when based on assumptions which are later corrected.
- Cost based on Defined Cost as defined in the Schedule of Cost Component.
- Time based on entitlement not need.
- Assessment to include *Contractor*'s risk allowances (clause 63.6).
- Remember a compensation event may create new risk matters which need to be included on the contract Risk Register.

B2.7 Shorter Schedule of Cost Components – example quotation

The Shorter Schedule of Cost Components is used to assess compensation events for main Options A and B. For main Options A, B, C, D and E in clause 63.11, if the *Project Manager* and *Contractor* agree, the *Contractor* assesses a compensation event using the Shorter Schedule of Cost Components.

ECC3 has simplified the SSCC for greater ease of use.

1. People
The people cost component has been simplified in item 11 to amounts paid by the *Contractor* including those for meeting the requirements of the law and the pension provisions.

Table B2.9 shows an extract of the people element of a quotation using the Shorter SCC.

2. Equipment
- Amounts for Equipment in the published list identified in Contract Data part two adjusted by the percentage adjustment listed in Contract Data part two. The published list for example will be the Civil Engineering Contractors Association Daywork Schedule, or RICS Daywork Schedule, etc.

The entry in Contract Data part two is as follows:

- The percentage for people overheads is 30%.

Note: An adjustment is required on Equipment listed in published lists, e.g. CECA Daywork, because the rates include for an element of overheads and profit in the listed rates which is included in the Fee.

- The published list of Equipment is the last edition of the list published by ......CECA ....

Table B2.9. Example extract of the people element of a quotation using the Shorter SCC

PEOPLE						
Activity F250 – Set up site (5 days)				Note: Hourly rates will be lower than in the full SCC.		
	No.	Hrs	Total hrs	Rate		
Foreman	1	24	24	12.00	288.00	
Labourers	4	40	160	10.00	1,600.00	
Ganger	1	40	40	7.00	280.00	2,168.00
Activity F300, etc.						10,000.00
			Total for people		= £	12,168.00
Note: See Table B2.10 for build-up for percentage for people overheads.		Percentage for people overheads + 30%				2,168.00
			TOTAL FOR PEOPLE		= £	14,336.00

- The percentage for adjustment for listed Equipments is .... −30% ....
- The rates for other Equipment are

Equipment	size or capacity	rate

- Amounts for Equipment listed in the Contract Data not in the published list. This is a list of Equipment inserted for Equipment required to provide the *works* which is not listed in the published list.

3. Plant and Materials
The same as the full Schedule of Cost Components.

4. Charges
Similar to Charges in the full Schedule of Cost Components. In the full SCC item 44 picks up a group of sundry costs; this is expressed as a percentage for people costs and is known as the Working Areas overheads percentage.

In the SSCC the costs identified separately in items 41, 42 and 43 are also included in a percentage applied to people costs and this is known as the percentage for people overheads.

As a general rule the percentage for people overheads should be greater than the Working Area overhead percentage because it includes more items.

An example for the calculation for percentage for people overheads is shown in Table B2.10.

5. Manufacture and fabrication
In ECC3 this has been simplified to Amounts paid by the *Contractor*.[226]

6. Design
The same as the full Schedule of Cost Components (see section B2.6.6 above).

7. Insurance
The same as the full Schedule of Cost Components.

8. Contractor's risk
The same as the full Schedule of Cost Components (see section B2.6.7 above).

---

[226]Clause 51 of SSCC.

Table B2.10. Example build-up for people percentage for Shorter Schedule of Cost Components

Item	Description		Non-time related	Time-related charge			
				Rate	Per	Duration	Total
(a) Overhead payments for people including payroll burdens							
	Shortfall in people components 12 and 13	£708.11 shortfall per year per direct employee – site has 30 people: £708.11/52 weeks = £13.61 per wk per employee × 50 = £680.50 per week		680.50	per employee	30 wks	20,415.00

Note: see Appendix 3 Table A3.4: Calculation of people cost.

			Non-time related	Rate	Per	Duration	Total
(b) Payments to utilities for the provision and use in the Working Areas of							
Provision							
	Water	connection charge	250.00				
		site installation	200.00				
		disconnection	100.00				
	Gas	connection charge	0.00				
		site installation	200.00				
		disconnection	0.00				
	Electricity	connection charge	250.00				
		site installation	200.00				
		disconnection	100.00				
Use of							
	Water	water supply charge	0.00	20.00	per wk	30 wks	600.00
	Gas	gas supply charge	0.00	0.00	per wk	0 mths	0.00
	Electricity	electricity supply charge	0.00	200.00	per wk	30 wks	6,000.00
(c) Payments to public authorities, utilities and other properly constituted authorities of charges which they are authorised to make in respect of the works							
(d) Payments for							
	Financing charges (excluding charges compensated for by interest paid in accordance with this contract)						
	Buying or leasing land	temporary lease of land for compound	2,500.00	—	—	—	—
	Compensation for loss of crops or buildings	compensation for loss of crops to Farmer Jones	1,000.00	—	—	—	—
	Royalties	royalties for use of patented paint for bridge	100.00	—	—	—	—
	Inspection certificates	building regulation inspections	250.00	—	—	—	—
	Rent of premises in the Working Areas	rent for site offices	—	10.00	per wk	30 wks	300.00
	Charges for access to the Working Areas	charge for access via wayleave to rear of site	500.00	—	—	—	—
	Facilities for visits to the Working Area by Others	visitors' PPE (personal protection equipment)	500.00	—	—	—	—
		furniture rental	—	10.00	per wk	30 wks	300.00
		TV and video rental	—	5.00	per wk	30 wks	150.00
	Specialist services		—	—	—	—	—
Payments for							
	Accommodation	10 office staff × 8 m² = 80 m²		120.00	per wk	30 wks	3,600.00
		canteen		40.00	per wk	31 wks	1,240.00
		washroom		25.00	per wk	32 wks	800.00
		staff toilets		30.00	per wk	33 wks	990.00
		site toilets		30.00	per wk	34 wks	1,020.00
	Equipment	office equipment	100.00	—	—	—	—
		testing equipment rental	—	10.00	per wk	30 wks	300.00
		fire-fighting equipment rental	—	10.00	per wk	30 wks	300.00
		camera rental	—	2.50	per wk	30 wks	75.00
		sign boards and traffic signs	500.00	—	—	—	—
	Supplies and services for offices	General Office expenditure – tea, milk, sugar, washing-up liquid, mugs, stationery, stamps, film, etc.	100.00	10.00	per wk	30 wks	300.00
		office cleaner (part-time)	—	25.00	per wk	30 wks	750.00
		furniture and equipment rental	—	35.00	per wk	30 wks	1,050.00
		c/f	£6,850.00				£40,890.00

Table B2.10. *Continued*

Item	Description		Non-time related	Time-related charge			
				Rate	Per	Duration	Total
		c/f	£6,850.00				£40,890.00
	furniture and office equipment – purchase price less residual value		500.00	—	—	—	—
Drawing office	general expenditure		—	—	—	—	—
Laboratories	general expenditure		—	20.00	per wk	30 wks	600.00
Workshops	general expenditure		—	20.00	per wk	30 wks	600.00
Stores and compounds	stores		—	20.00	per wk	30 wks	600.00
	general expenditure		—	20.00	per wk	30 wks	600.00
Labour camps	Note: particularly relevant on international projects.		—	—	—	—	—
Cabins	general expenditure		—	—	—	—	—
	Note: assumed that this will include *Contractor*'s welfare facilities which are not specifically mentioned in component 41.						
Catering	catering services provided by Well Feed Limited		—	200.00	per wk	30 wks	6,000.00
Medical facilities and first aid	medical equipment and supplies		500.00	—	—	—	—
Recreation	five-a-side football pitch — Note: particularly relevant on international projects.						
Sanitation	cess pit cleaning		—	10.00	per wk	30 wks	300.00
Security	site security guard		—	80.00	per wk	30 wks	2,400.00
	security hut and barriers		—	50.00	per wk	30 wks	1,500.00
	site hoarding and lighting – set-up and removal		1,000.00	—	—	—	—
Copying	photocopier monthly hire charge		—	5.00	per wk	30 wks	150.00
Telephone	installation and disconnection		200.00	—	—	—	—
	monthly telephone bills		—	20.00	per wk	30 wks	600.00
Fax	installation and disconnection of dedicated phone line		200.00	—	—	—	—
	monthly telephone line bills		—	10.00	per wk	30 wks	300.00
Radio	provision of 10 No. hand-held radios		500.00	—	—	—	—
CCTV	installation of CCTV cameras to site perimeter 10 No. and control system		500.00	—	—	—	—
	removal of CCTV cameras on completion		200.00	—	—	—	—
	provision of CCTV tapes		100.00	—	—	—	—
Surveying and setting out	survey equipment rental		—	20.00	per wk	30 wks	600.00
	purchase cost pegs, paint, profiles, etc.		250.00	—	—	—	—
Computing	provision of 2 No. office computers		1,000.00				
	purchase of planning software		300.00				
	installation of ADSL line		100.00				
	rental for ADSL line		—	5.00	per wk	30 wks	150.00
	printers 2		500.00	—	—	—	—
	printer ink cartridges		—	5.00	per wk	30 wks	150.00
Hand tools and hand-held power tools + A52	small tools, say 1% of labour costs (assume labour costs £150,000) say		1,000.00	—	—	—	—
Subtotals	**Non-time-related costs to summary = £**		**13,700.00**	**Time-related costs to summary = £**			**55,440.00**

Summary		£
Non-time-related	£	13,700.00
Time-related	£	55,440.00
Total cost for component 41	**£**	**£69,140.00**

Contract breakdown

Labour	250,000.00
Materials	150,000.00
Equipment (constructional plant)	150,000.00
Profit	50,000.00
Total contract value	**£600,000.00**

Calculation for percentage for people overheads $\quad \dfrac{69,140.00}{250,000.00} \times \dfrac{1.00}{100.00}$

Percentage for people overheads $\quad = \quad \underline{\underline{27.66\%}}$

say $\quad = \quad \underline{\underline{30\%}}$

Table B2.11. Example quotation using the Shorter Schedule of Cost Components

CONTRACT: SPRING FIELD								

QUOTATION FOR COMPENSATION EVENT
SHORTER SCHEDULE OF COST COMPONENTS   **SHORTER**

To: Project Manager   No: 41

From: Virtual Contracting Limited   Sheet: 1

Brief Description of Works: Provision of Footbridge to Spring Dyke Due to Road Realignment   Date: 1st July 2005

ACTIVITY NO./NOS:
A500   **DELAY TO PLANNED COMPLETION:**
1 Day   SECTION OF WORKS AFFECTED:
3A

1. PEOPLE

Activity 500 – kerbing to roads and footpaths

	No.	Days	Total days	Hrs	Total hrs	Rate		
Foreman	1	2	2	10	20	15.00	300.00	
Labourer	2	2	4	10	40	10.00	400.00	

Note: See example Contract Data part two – data provided by the *Contractor*: Data for the Shorter Schedule of Cost Components and example people % build-up in Table A3.3.

Subtotal   700.00
Percentage for people percentage +28%   196.00

PEOPLE TOTAL CARRIED TO SUMMARY =   **£896.00**

2. EQUIPMENT

Notes: Rates for Equipment taken from published list stated in Contract Data part two, e.g. CECA Daywork Schedule.

Activity 500 – kerbing to roads and footpaths

	No.	Days	Total days	Hrs	Total hrs	Rate		
Dumper	1	2	2	10	20	20.00	400.00	
Lorry	1	2	2	10	20	20.00	400.00	

Note: See example Contract Data part two: Data for the Shorter Schedule of Cost Components.

Subtotal   800.00
Equipment adjustment −30%   240.00

The rates for other listed Equipment

Note: See example Contract Data part two: Data for the Shorter Schedule of Cost Components.

0.00

EQUIPMENT TOTAL CARRIED TO SUMMARY =   **£560.00**

3. PLANT AND MATERIALS

Activity 500 – kerbing to roads and footpaths

	No.	Rate		
Standard kerbs	20	20.00	400.00	
Drop kerbs	4	50.00	200.00	
				600.00

PLANT AND MATERIALS TOTAL CARRIED TO SUMMARY =   **£600.00**

4. CHARGES (included in people percentage added to item 1 People above)   **£00.00**

5. MANUFACTURE AND FABRICATION OUTSIDE OF THE WORKING AREAS

None
Employee costs   £

Note: See Contract Data part two data provided by the *Contractor* – Data for Schedule of Cost Components.

Subtotal
Manufacture and fabrication overhead +20%

MANUFACTURE AND FABRICATION OUTSIDE OF THE WORKING AREAS TOTAL CARRIED TO SUMMARY =   **£ 00.00**

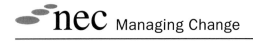
nec Managing Change

Table B2.11. *Continued*

6. DESIGN OUTSIDE OF THE WORKING AREAS		
None		
Employee costs £		
Subtotal		
Note: see Contract Data part two data provided by the *Contractor* – Data for Schedule of Cost Components. — Design overhead +30%		
DESIGN OUTSIDE OF THE WORKING AREAS TOTAL CARRIED TO SUMMARY		£ 00.00
7. INSURANCES		
None		
INSURANCES TOTAL CARRIED TO SUMMARY		£ 00.00
8. CONTRACTOR'S TIME/RISK ALLOWANCES — Note: See example time/risk schedule in Table B2.6.		
None		
CONTRACTOR'S TIME/RISK ALLOWANCES TOTAL CARRIED TO SUMMARY		£ 00.00

SUMMARY	£
1. PEOPLE	896.00
2. EQUIPMENT	560.00
3. PLANT AND MATERIALS	600.00
4. CHARGES	0.00
5. MANUFACTURE AND FABRICATION	0.00
6. DESIGN	0.00
7. INSURANCES	0.00
8. CONTRACTOR'S TIME/RISK ALLOWANCES	0.00
Subtotal	£2,056.00
9. FEE *Fee percentage* 10% Note: See example Contract Data part two – data provided by the *Contractor* in section A2.2 above.	205.60
Grand Total =	**£2,261.60**

Appendix 3 Example people cost calculations – ECC2 and ECC3

A3.1 Introduction

This appendix looks at the comparison of how people (labour costs) would be calculated traditionally by contractors and how this compares to the Schedule of Cost Components and the Shorter Schedule of Cost Components for both ECC2 and ECC3.

It also shows how these costs interact with each other and how they can be calculated and dealt with.

A3.2 ECC2 only

Table A3.1 compares side by side the FSCC and a traditional build-up. It highlights the differences between the two calculations and indicates how these differences in the costs are to be dealt with when using the FSCC.

Table A3.2 compares side by side the SSCC and a traditional build-up. It highlights the differences between the two calculations and indicates how these differences in the costs are to be dealt with when using the SSCC.

It also indicates the differences between the FSCC and SCCC and refers you to Table A3.3 for an example calculation on how to deal with these components of cost.

Table A3.3 gives an example of a calculation to determine the percentage needed within the people percentage for the SSCC to cover those items of people costs which are not included in the SSCC but are included as separate items in the FSCC, namely items of cost 12(e) to (f) and 13(c) to (o).

A3.3 ECC3 only

Table A3.4 compares side by side the FSCC and a traditional build-up. It highlights the differences between the two calculations and indicates how these differences in the costs are to be dealt with when using the FSCC.

The equivalent Tables A3.2 and A3.3 shown for ECC2 are not relevant in ECC3 (item 11 of the SSCC), as in the SSCC the *Contractor* is paid:

> '11 Amounts paid by the Contractor including those for meeting the requirements of the law and for pension provision.'

Table A3.1. Calculation of people costs – side-by-side comparison of full Schedule of Cost Components and traditional calculation of labour costs (ECC2)

Rate build-up based on full Schedule of Cost Components			Traditional calculation for labour costs **Annual cost of wages** (Based on Construction Industry Joint Council – Working Rule Agreement)			
11 **Wages and salary** *(Figure made up of Basic Rate, Additional Payments for skill, National Insurance and Training Levy Allowance from traditional build-up opposite)*			Basic rate of pay (Classification – General Operative, skill rate 1, 2, 3, 4, Craft Rate)			
1) Basic salary	12,877.32	14,723.10		2694 hrs @ 4.78		12,877.32
2) NI	1,757.89		Additional payment for skilled	0 hrs @ 4.78		
3) Training levy	87.89		work WRA Schedule 1 –			
	£14,723.10		Classification i, ii, iii			0.00
12 **Payments for**						
(a) bonuses and incentives		2,694.00	Bonus – guaranteed minimum and production bonus	2694 hrs @ 1.00		2,694.00
(b) overtime		2,007.60	Non-productive overtime	420 hrs @ 4.78		2,007.60
				Annual wage (A)		17,578.92
		incl. in 11	National Insurance, employer's contribution @ 10% of (A)			1,757.89
		incl. in 11	Training Allowance or Industrial Training Levy, e.g. CITB Training Levy 0.50% of PAYE (A)			87.89
(c) working in special circumstances			WRA Schedule 2 – Working in adverse conditions, e.g. stone cleaning, tunnels, sewer work, working at height			
		0.00				0.00
(d) special allowances						
(e) absence due to sickness and holidays		1,230.85	Holiday credit	52 wks @ 23.67		1,230.85
		351.58	Sick pay allowance @ 2% of (A) above			351.58
			Paid total and allowances (B)			21,007.13
(f) + A23 severance related to work on this contract		315.11	Allowance for severance pay 1.5% of (B)			315.11
13 **Payments in relation to people for**						
(a) travelling to and from the Working Areas		0.00	WR.5 Travel allowances			0.00
(b) subsistence and lodging			WR.15 Subsistence (where applicable)			
		5,974.64	47 weeks × 7 nights × £18.16 per night			5,974.64
(c) relocation						0.00
(d) medical examinations						0.00
(e) passport and visas						0.00
(f) travel insurance						0.00
(g) items (a) to (f) for a spouse or dependants						0.00
(h) protective clothing		105.04	Protective clothing 0.50% of (B)			105.04
(j) meeting the requirements of the law			Employer's liability and public liability insurance 2% of (B)			
		420.14				420.14
(k) superannuation and life insurance		0.00	Industry Pension Scheme			0.00
(l) death benefit		50.00	WR.21 Benefit schemes (Death Benefit Stamp)		say	50.00
(m) occupational accident benefits						
(n) medical aid		452.51	Health insurance		say	452.51
		0.00	Vehicle (assumed dealt with separately)			
		0.00	Safety Training (demonstration on ongoing commitment to safety)			
Total annual cost =	£	**28,324.57**	*Total annual cost =*		£	**28,324.57**
	These items need to be included in the *fee percentage*		Safety officer's time, QA Policy/inspection and all other costs and overheads say 2.5% Note: These items are included in the calculation of labour costs using the Working Rule Agreement but are not a Component of People Costs in the ECC			708.11
Total annual cost of general operative =	£	**28,324.57**	*Total annual cost of general operative =*		£	**29,032.68**
Total hours worked =	£	**2,694.00**	*Total hours worked =*		£	**2,694.00**
Cost per hour =	£	**10.51**	*Cost per hour =*		£	**10.78**

Note: The difference between the rate of £10.51 in the Schedule of Cost Component build-up and the £10.78 in the traditional build-up is the £708.11. This is included in the *fee percentage* in the SCC Table 2.3 in Chapter 2.

Table A3.2. Calculation of people costs – side-by-side comparison of Shorter Schedule of Cost Components and traditional calculation of labour costs

Rate build-up based on the Shorter Schedule of Cost Components		Traditional calculation for labour costs Annual cost of wages (Based on Construction Industry Joint Council – Working Rule Agreement)			
11 Wages and salary *(Figure made up of Basic Rate, Additional Payments for skill, National Insurance and Training Levy Allowance)*	14,723.10	Basic rate of pay (Classification – General Operative, Skill Rate 1, 2, 3, 4, Craft Rate)	2694 hrs @ 4.78		12,877.32
1) Basic salary 12,877.32		Additional payment for skilled work WRA Schedule 1 – Classification i, ii, iii	0 hrs @ 4.78		0.00
2) NI 1,757.89					
3) Training levy 87.89					
£14,723.10					
12 Payments for					
(a) bonuses and incentives	2,694.00	Bonus – guaranteed minimum and production bonus	2694 hrs @ 1.00		2,694.00
(b) overtime	2,007.60	Non-productive overtime	420 hrs @ 4.78		2,007.60
			Annual wage (A)		17,578.92
	incl. in 11	National Insurance employer's contribution @ 10% of (A)			1,757.89
	incl. in 11	Training Allowance or Industrial Training Levy, e.g. CITB Training Levy 0.50% of PAYE (A)			87.89
The items of cost below A41 now go to item **4 Charges** to form part of the people percentage which is added to the cost of people					
(c) working in special circumstances (FSCC £0.00) [Note: See Table A3.3 for example of calculation for percentage addition for the people percentage.]		WRA Schedule 2 – Working in adverse conditions, e.g. stone cleaning, tunnels, sewer work, working at height			0.00
(d) special allowances (FSCC £0.00)					
(e) absence due to sickness and holidays (FSCC £1,230.84 plus £351.58)		Holiday credit	52 wks @ 23.67		1,230.85
		Sick pay allowance @ 2% of (A) above			351.58
		Paid total and allowances (B)			21,007.13
(f) severance related to work on this contract (FSCC £315.11)		Allowance for severance pay 1.5% of (B)			315.11
(Total to be carried to people % = £1,897.53)					
13 Payments in relation to people for					
(a) travelling to and from the Working Areas	0.00	WR.5 Travel allowances			0.00
(b) subsistence and lodging	5,974.64	WR.15 Subsistence (where applicable) 47 weeks × 7 nights × £18.16 per night			5,974.64
These items of cost below now go to item **4 Charges** to form part of the people percentage which is added to the cost of people					0.00
(d) medical examinations (FSCC £0.00)					0.00
(e) passport and visas (FSCC £0.00)					0.00
(f) travel insurance (FSCC £0.00) [Note: See Table A3.3 for example of calculation for percentage addition for the people percentage.]					0.00
(g) items (a) to (f) for a spouse or dependants (FSCC £0.00)					0.00
(h) protective clothing (FSCC £105.04)		Protective clothing 0.50% of (B)			105.04
(j) meeting the requirements of the law (FSCC £420.14)		Employers liability and public liability insurance 2% of (B)			420.14
(k) superannuation and life insurance (FSCC £0.00)		Industry Pension Scheme			0.00
(l) death benefit (FSCC £50.00)		WR.21 Benefit schemes (Death Benefit Stamp)		say	50.00
(m) occupational accident benefits (FSCC £0.00)					
(n) medical aid (FSCC £452.51)		Health insurance		say	452.51
(Total to be carried to people % = £1,027.69)					
Total Annual Cost = £ **25,399.34** (Note: The difference between SCCC and traditional build-up = £28,324.57 less £25,399.34 = £2,925.23. See Table A3.3 which shows how this cost is included in the percentage for people overheads)	These items need to be included in the fee percentage	***Total Annual Cost =*** £ **28,324.57** Safety officer's time, QA Policy/inspection and all other costs and overheads say 2.5% Note: These items are included in the calculation of labour costs using the Working Rule Agreement but are not a Component of People Costs in the ECC			
					708.11
Total annual cost of general operative =	£ 25,399.34	***Total annual cost of general operative =***		£	29,032.68
Total hours worked =	£ 2,694.00	***Total hours worked =***		£	2,694.00
Cost per hour =	£ 9.45	***Cost per hour =***		£	10.78

Note: The difference between £9.43 in the Shorter Schedule of Cost Components and £10.78 in the traditional build-up is the item of £708.11 in the traditional build-up which will need to go into the calculation of the *fee percentage* (see Table 2.3 in Chapter 2 for an example of how to include it in the calculation of the *fee percentage*) and the items in items 12 and 13 which are not separately listed in the Shorter Schedule of Cost Components totalling £2,925.23 made up of £1,897.53 for items 12(c) to (f) £1,027.69 for items 13(d) to (n), (see Table A3.3 for an example of how to calculate this element of the percentage for people overheads).

Table A3.3. Calculation of the percentage for people overheads – part of the percentage for people overheads for the Shorter Schedule of Cost Components (see SCC Charges 4(a))

Charges 4(a)

The following is a list of items for people costs that are not included in the Shorter Schedule of Cost Components	£
12 **Payments for**	
(e) absence due to sickness and holidays	1,230.84
	351.58
(f) severance related to work on this contract	315.11
13 **Payments in relation to people for**	
(c) relocation	
(d) medical examinations	
(e) passport and visas	
(f) travel insurance	
(g) items (a) to (f) for a spouse or dependants	
(h) protective clothing	105.04
(j) meeting the requirements of the law	420.14
(k) superannuation and life insurance	0
(l) death benefit	50.00
(m) occupational accident benefits	
(n) medical aid	452.51
Total cost of items excluded from Shorter Schedule of Cost Components =	2,925.23
Total hours worked =	2,694.00
Shortfall between full and Shorter Schedule of Cost Components £ per hour	£ 1.09
	0.10
Percentage addition required for People as part of item 4 Charges =	10%
	0.01
Percentage addition required for People as part of item 4 Charges =	10%

Traditional rate build-up = £10.78 per hour which includes £708.11 of costs included in the fee *percentage* in ECC2 (see Table A3.1 of this appendix)

The adjusted hourly rate is therefore £10.78 less £708.11/2694 working hours = £10.51 per hour compared to the Shorter Schedule of Cost Components rate of £9.43 per hour. The difference between these two figures is £1.09 per hour or circa 10%.

This percentage will form part of the peoples percentage which will be added to the cost of people in the Shorter Schedule of Cost Componenets. See item 4 Charges in the Shorter Schedule of Cost Components.

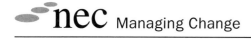

Table A3.4. Calculation of people costs – side-by-side comparison of full Schedule of Cost Components and traditional calculation of labour costs, ECC3 only

Rate build-up based on full Schedule of Cost Components		Traditional calculation for labour costs Annual cost of wages (Based on Construction Industry Joint Council – Working Rule Agreement)				
11 **Wages and salary** *(Figure made up of Basic Rate, Additional Payments for skill, National Insurance and Training Levy Allowance from traditional build-up opposite)*	14,723.10	Basic rate of pay (Classification – General Operative, skill rate 1, 2, 3, 4, Craft Rate)	2694 hrs	@	4.78	12,877.32
		Additional payment for skilled work WRA Schedule 1 – Classification i, ii, iii	0 hrs	@	4.78	0.00
12 **Payments for**						
(a) bonuses and incentives	2,694.00	Bonus – guaranteed minimum and production bonus	2694 hrs	@	1.00	2,694.00
(b) overtime	2,007.60	Non-productive overtime	420 hrs	@	4.78	2,007.60
			Annual wage (A)			17,578.92
	incl. in 11	National Insurance, employer's contribution @ 10% of (A)				1,757.89
	incl. in 11	Training Allowance or Industrial Training Levy, e.g. CITB Training Levy 0.50% of PAYE (A)				87.89
(c) working in special circumstances		WRA Schedule 2 – Working in adverse conditions, e.g. stone cleaning, tunnels, sewer work, working at height				
	0.00					0.00
(d) special allowances (e) absence due to sickness and holidays	1,230.85	Holiday credit	52 wks	@	23.67	1,230.85
	351.58	Sick pay allowance @ 2% of (A) above				351.58
			Paid total and allowances (B)			21,007.13
(f) + A23 severance related to work on this contract	315.11	Allowance for severance pay 1.5% of (B)				315.11
13 **Payments in relation to people for**						
(a) travelling to and from the Working Areas	0.00	WR.5 Travel allowances				0.00
(b) subsistence and lodging	5,974.64	WR.15 Subsistence (where applicable) 47 weeks × 7 nights × £18.16 per night				5,974.64
(c) relocation						0.00
(d) medical examinations						0.00
(e) passport and visas						0.00
(f) travel insurance						0.00
(g) items (a) to (f) for a spouse or dependants						0.00
(h) protective clothing	105.04	Protective clothing 0.50% of (B)				105.04
(j) meeting the requirements of the law	420.14	Employer's liability and public liability insurance 2% of (B)				420.14
(k) superannuation and life insurance	0.00	Industry Pension Scheme				0.00
(l) death benefit	50.00	WR.21 Benefit schemes (Death Benefit Stamp)		say		50.00
(m) occupational accident benefits						
(n) medical aid	452.51	Health insurance		say		452.51
	0.00	Vehicle (assumed dealt with separately)				
	0.00	Safety Training (demonstration on ongoing commitment to safety)				
Total annual cost =	£ 28,324.57	*Total annual cost =*			£	28,324.57
	These items need to be included in the *fee percentage*	Safety officer's time, QA Policy/inspection and all other costs and overheads say 2.5% Note: These items are included in the calculation of labour costs using the Working Rule Agreement but are not a Component of People Costs in the ECC				708.11
Total annual cost of general operative =	£ 28,324.57	*Total annual cost of general operative =*			£	29,032.68
Total hours worked =	£ 2,694.00	*Total hours worked =*			£	2,694.00
Cost per hour =	£ 10.51	*Cost per hour =*			£	10.78

Note: The difference between the rate of £10.51 in the Schedule of Cost Component Build-up and the £10.78 in the traditional build-up is the £708.11. This is included in the *direct fee percentage* in the SCC Table 2.3 in Chapter 2.

Appendix 4 Comparison between traditional preliminaries build-up and how they relate to the Schedule of Cost Components and the Shorter Schedule of Cost Components – for ECC2 and ECC3

A4.1 Introduction

This appendix aims to clarify by way of comparison how a traditional preliminaries build-up and the ECC relate to each other. In particular a traditional example build-up of preliminaries is given. This is then compared to the full and Shorter Schedule of Cost Components to show how they are dealt with in ECC2 and ECC3. (See Table A4.1.)

Table A4.1. Comparison between traditional tender build-up for staff, site on-costs and other items and how and where they are included in the ECC full Schedule of Cost Components and the Shorter Schedule of Cost Components, ECC2

Item description		£	ECC2 only		ECC3 only	
Contractor's Site on-costs – time-related			Full SCC	SSCC	Full SCC	SSCC
Site staff salaries						
Agent	30 wks	£450	13,500.00	People	People	People	People
Senior engineer	30 wks	£380	11,400.00	People	People	People	People
Engineers	30 wks	£300	9,000.00	People	People	People	People
General foreman	30 wks	£400	12,000.00	People	People	People	People
Office manager	30 wks	£400	12,000.00	People	People	People	People
Timekeeper	30 wks	£240	7,200.00	People	People	People	People
Storeman/checker	30 wks	£200	6,000.00	People	People	People	People
Typist/telephonist	30 wks	£150	4,500.00	People	People	People	People
Cost clerk	30 wks	£240	7,200.00	People	People	People	People
Quantity surveyor	30 wks	£450	13,500.00	People	People	People	People
Fitter						
Site staff expenses (1% of staff salaries)			People	People	People	People
Attendant labour						
Chainman	30 wks	£190	5,700.00	People	People	People	People
Driver	30 wks	£220	6,600.00	People	People	People	People
				Charges 4 (44) Part of WA OH %	Charges 4(a) part of People %	Charges 4 (44) Part of WA OH %	Charges 41 part of People %
Office cleaner (part-time)	30 wks	£80	2,400.00				
General yard labour (loading and offloading, clearing site, rubbish, etc)						
Ganger – 1 No.	30 wks	£220	6,600.00	People	People	People	People
Labourer – 2 No.	30 wks	£220	6,600.00	People	People	People	People
Plant Maintenance (contractor's own plant)						
Fitter	30 wks	£350	10,500.00	People	People	People	People
Fitters mate	30 wks	£300	9,000.00	People	People	People	People
Total Carried Forward =		£	143,700.00				

Note: ECC2 only – admissible if these salaried staff are full time on Site and dedicated to the contract. ECC3 people who are not directly employed but are working in the Working Area are paid according to time worked while they are in the Working Areas.

Note: WA OH% refers to the Working Areas overhead percentage.

Table A4.1. *Continued*

Item description		£	ECC2 only Full SCC	ECC2 only SSCC	ECC3 only Full SCC	ECC3 only SSCC	Notes
Contractor's Site on-costs – time-related							
Total Brought Forward	£	143,700.00					
Site transport – staff							Note: ECC2 – these are either provided as part of the project costs or they may already be included in the cost of People if they are part of a person's employment package.
Agent's car	30 wks £100	3,000.00	*Equipment	*Equipment	*Equipment/People item 13(n)	*Equipment/People item 11	
Engineer's car	30 wks £90	2,700.00	*Equipment	*Equipment	*Equipment/People item 13(n)	*Equipment/People item 11	
Land Rover (for general use on Site)	30 wks £150	4,500.00	Equipment	Equipment	Equipment	Equipment	ECC3 – see FSCC item 13(n) vehicle.
Site transport – labour							
Bus – two trips per day	30 wks £250	7,500.00	Equipment	Equipment	Equipment	Equipment	
Contractor's offices							
Mobile office (10 staff × 8 m² = 80 m²)	30 wks £120	3,600.00	WA OH %	People%	Equipment	Equipment	
Section offices (1 No. at 10 m²)	30 wks £30	900.00	WA OH %	People%	Equipment	Equipment	
Contractor's site huts							
Stores hot 30 m²	30 wks £20	600.00	WA OH %	People%	Equipment	Equipment	
Canteen 70 m²	30 wks £100	3,000.00	WA OH %	People%	Equipment	Equipment	
Washroom 30 m²	30 wks £25	750.00	WA OH %	People%	Equipment	Equipment	
Staff toilets	30 wks £30	900.00	WA OH %	People%	Equipment	Equipment	
Site toilets	30 wks £30	900.00	WA OH %	People%	Equipment	Equipment	
Rates		Nil	Charges				
General							Note: The requirement to clean the roads may mean the public highway which may be outside of the Working Areas/Site. The Contractor should ensure that a Working Area is identified for this requirement as part of his obligation to provide the works.
General office expenditure	30 wks £50	1,500.00	WA OH %	People%	WA OH %	People%	
Telephone calls and rental	30 wks £50	1,500.00	WA OH %	People%	WA OH %	People%	
Furniture rental	30 wks £35	1,050.00	WA OH %	People%	WA OH %	People%	
Canteen and welfare rental	30 wks £40	1,200.00	WA OH %	People%	WA OH %	People%	
Surveying equipment rental	30 wks £30	900.00	WA OH %	People%	WA OH %	People%	
Testing equipment rental	30 wks £25	750.00	WA OH %	People%	WA OH %	People%	
Lighting and heating offices	30 wks £45	1,350.00	Charges 41 (c)	People%	Charges 41 (c)	Charges 43	
Water supply	30 wks £20	600.00	Charges 41 (a)	People%	Charges 41 (a)	Charges 43	This is important since the Contractor is only paid for the consequences of compensation events within the Working Areas.
Small tools (1% of labour cost)	say	5,000.00	WA OH %	People%	WA OH %	People%	
Protective clothing (0.5% on labour cost)	say	2,500.00	People	People%	People	People%	
Road lighting							
Cleaning roads							
Road sweeper	30 wks £50	1,500.00	Equipment	Equipment	Equipment	Equipment	
Labour	30 wks £150	4,500.00	People	People	People	People	
Progress photographs	say	1,000.00	Charges 4 Part of WA OH %	Charges 4(e) part of People %	Charges 4 Part of WA OH %	Charges 41 part of People %	
Total Contractor's Site on-costs – time-related =	£	195,400.00					

Table A4.1. *Continued*

Item description	£	ECC2 only		ECC3 only	
		Full SCC	SSCC	Full SCC	SSCC
Contractor's Site on-costs – non-time-related					
(These costs are unlikely to be affected by compensation events)					
Erect and dismantle offices					
Mobile	say 500.00	WA OH %	People%	Equipment	Equipment
Site offices	say 500.00	WA OH %	People%	Equipment	Equipment
Toilets	say 500.00	WA OH %	People%	Equipment	Equipment
Wiring, water, etc.	say 500.00	WA OH %	People%	Equipment	Equipment
Erect and dismantle other buildings					
Stores	say 500.00	WA OH %	People%	Equipment	Equipment
Welfare	say 500.00	WA OH %	People%	Equipment	Equipment
Toilets	say 500.00	WA OH %	People%	Equipment	Equipment
Wiring, water, etc.	say 500.00	WA OH %	People%	Equipment	Equipment
Telephone Installation	say 500.00	WA OH %	People%	WA OH %	People%
Furniture and office equipment (Purchase cost less residual value)	say 500.00	WA OH %	People%	WA OH %	People%
Survey equipment and setting out Purchase cost, pegs, paint, profiles, etc.	say 700.00	WA OH %	People%	WA OH %	People%
Canteen and welfare equipment Purchase cost less residual value	say 1,500.00	WA OH %	People%	WA OH %	People%
Electrical installation					
Water supply					
Connection charges	say 500.00	Charges	People%	Charges	Charges 43
Site installation	say 500.00	WA OH %	People%	WA OH %	Charges 43
Transport of plant and equipment	say 500.00	Equipment	Equipment	Equipment	Equipment
Stores compounds and huts	say 500.00	WA OH %	People%	Equipment	Equipment
Sign boards and traffic signs	say 500.00	Equipment	Equipment	Equipment	Equipment
Insurances					
Contractors ALL risk (1.5% on £500k)	7,500.00	fee % People?	fee %	*direct fee %*	*direct fee %*
Allow for excesses	2,000.00	fee % People?	fee %	*direct fee %*	*direct fee %*
General Site clearance	say 1,500.00	WA OH %	People%	People/ Equipment	People/ Equipment
Total Contractor's Site on-costs – non-time-related =	£ 20,700.00				

Table A4.1. *Continued*

Employer's and Consultant's requirements on site – time-related

(Details of the requirements will be defined in the Works Information) Note: These items refer to items to be provided by the Contractor for use by the Employer and his team on the contract.

Item description		£	ECC2 only		ECC3 only	
			Full SCC	SSCC	Full SCC	SSCC
Attendant labour	30 wks	100.00	People	People	People	People
Offices 40 m²	30 wks	100.00	WA OH %	People%	Equipment	Equipment
Transport 2 Landrovers	30 wks	300.00	Equipment	Equipment	Equipment	Equipment
Telephone calls and rental	30 wks	25.00	WA OH %	People%	WA OH %	People%
Furniture and Equipment	30 wks	25.00	WA OH %	People%	WA OH %	People%
Survey equipment	30 wks	25.00	WA OH %	People%	WA OH %	People%
Heating and lighting 40 m²	30 wks	30.00	WA OH %	People%	WA OH %	People%
Office consumables	30 wks	20.00	WA OH %	People%	WA OH %	People%
Office cleaning	30 wks	20.00	WA OH %	People%	WA OH %	People%
Total Employer's and Contractor's requirements – time-related =		**£ 19,350.00**				

Employer's and Consultant's requirements on site – non-time-related

(Details of the requirements will be defined in the Works Information)

Note: These items refer to items to be provided by the Contractor for use by the Employer and his team on the contract.

Item description		£	ECC2 only		ECC3 only	
			Full SCC	SSCC	Full SCC	SSCC
Erection and dismantling of engineer's offices	say	500.00	WA OH %	People%	WA OH %	People%
Toilets	say	250.00	WA OH %	People%	WA OH %	People%
Telephone installation	say	200.00	WA OH %	People%	WA OH %	People%
Electrical installation	say	200.00	WA OH %	People%	WA OH %	People%
Furniture and Equipment (Purchase price less residual value)	say	2,000.00	WA OH %	People%	WA OH %	People%
Progress photographs	say	250.00	WA OH %	People%	WA OH %	People%
Total Employer's and Consultant's requirements – time-related =		**£ 3,400.00**				

Temporary works not included in unit rates

Item description			£	ECC2 only		ECC3 only	
				Full SCC	SSCC	Full SCC	SSCC
Temporary fencing 500 m chestnut fencing – materials	500 m	10	5,000.00	Plant and Materials	Plant and Materials	Plant and Materials	Plant and Materials
Plant	say		1,000.00	Equipment	Equipment	Equipment	Equipment
Labour	200 man hrs	10	2,000.00	People	People	People	People
Traffic diversions	say		2,000.00	People/P&M/ Equipment	People/P&M/ Equipment	People/P&M/ Equipment	People/P&M/ Equipment
Footpath diversion	say		500.00	People/P&M/ Equipment	People/P&M/ Equipment	People/P&M/ Equipment	People/P&M/ Equipment
Site Access Roads	say		4,000.00	People/P&M/ Equipment	People/P&M/ Equipment	People/P&M/ Equipment	People/P&M/ Equipment
Total temporary works not included in unit rates =			**£ 14,500.00**				

Table A4.1. *Continued*

General purpose plant and plant not included in unit costs			£	ECC2 only Full SCC	ECC2 only SSCC	ECC3 only Full SCC	ECC3 only SSCC
Wheeled tractor							
Hire	30 wks	240	7,200.00	Equipment (21 externally hired or 22 Internally hired)	Equipment (published schedule or list in Contract Data)	Equipment (21 externally hired or 22 Internally hired)	Equipment (published schedule or list in Contract Data)
Driver	30 wks	1250	37,500.00	People (unless included in hire rates or depreciation and maintenance charge – item 25)	People (unless included in hire charge – item 26)	People (unless included in hire rates or depreciation and maintenance charge – item 28)	People (unless included in hire charge – item 26)
Consumables	30 wks	50	1,500.00	Equipment (item 23 the purchase price of Equipment which is consumed)	Equipment (item 24 and 25)	Equipment (item 25 the purchase price of Equipment which is consumed)	Equipment (item 25 the purchase price of Equipment which is consumed)
22 RB Crane							
Hire	30 wks	250	7,500.00	Equipment	Equipment	Equipment	Equipment
Driver	30 wks	1250	37,500.00	People	People	People	People
Consumables	30 wks	50	1,500.00	Equipment	Equipment	Equipment	Equipment
Sawbench							
Hire	30 wks	30	900.00	Equipment	Equipment	Equipment	Equipment
Consumables	30 wks	10	300.00	Equipment	Equipment	Equipment	Equipment
Compressor 21 m³ silenced							
Hire	30 wks	200	6,000.00	Equipment	Equipment	Equipment	Equipment
Consumables	30 wks	20	600.00	Equipment	Equipment	Equipment	Equipment
Pumps							
Hire	30 wks	50	1,500.00	Equipment	Equipment	Equipment	Equipment
Consumables	30 wks	20	600.00	Equipment	Equipment	Equipment	Equipment

Total general purpose constructional plant not included in unit costs = £ 102,600.00

Appendix 5 Interrelationship between *Contractor*'s and Subcontractor's *share* on target cost contracts

A5.1 Introduction

This appendix aims to clarify by way of an example the interrelationship between the *Contractor*'s and Subcontractor's *share* on target cost contracts.

Table A5.1 shows how the *Contractor*'s share is calculated in an ECC2 contract and Table A5.2 shows the same calculation for ECC3.

Table A5.1. ECC2 – Interrelationship between *Contractor*'s and *Subcontractor*'s share on target contracts (assuming that the PWDD is less than the total of the Prices)

Main Contractor ECC Option C or D Target Cost Contract			Subcontractor A ECC Subcontract Option C or D Target Cost Contract		
Contractor's share 50/50 of the difference between the total of the Prices (target) and the Price for Work Done to Date (Defined Cost)			*Subcontractor's share* 50/50 of the difference between the total of the Prices (target) and the Price for Work Done to Date (Actual Cost)		
			Subcontractor's share 50% of under or overspend		
		£			£
Total of the Prices (target cost)		210,000.00	Total of the Prices (target cost)		200,000.00
(£200,000.00 from Subcontractor plus *Contractor's* fee percentage of 10% = £212,000.00)					
Price for Work Done to Date (Actual Cost)		192,500.00	Price for Work Done to Date (Actual Cost)		150,000.00
(£175,000.00 from subcontractor plus *Contractor's* fee percentage of 10% = £192,500.00)					
Difference (saving)	(A)	27,500.00	Difference (saving)	(A)	50,000.00
Calculation for the Actual Cost		£	**Calculation for the Actual Cost**		£
Price for Work Done to Date (Defined Cost)		192,500.00	Price for Work Done to Date (Actual Cost)		150,000.00
Contractor's share (Difference between total of the Prices and the Price for Work Done to Date) from (A) above			*Contractor's share* (Difference between total of the Prices and the Price for Work Done to Date) from (A) above		
27,500.00 × 50%		13,750.00	50,000 × 50%		25,000.00
Total paid to *Contractor* = (by *Employer* to *Contractor*)	£	206,250.00	**Total paid to *Subcontractor* =** (by *Contractor* to *Subcontractor*)	£	175,000.00

Note: Subcontractor's total of the prices (target cost) is used in the *Contractor's* build for the total of the prices (target cost).

Table A5.2. ECC3 – Interrelationship between *Contractor's* and *Subcontractor's* share on target contracts (assuming that the PWDD is less than the total of the Prices)

Main Contractor ECC Option C or D Target Cost Contract	Subcontractor A ECC Subcontract Option C or D Target Cost Contract
Contractor's share 50/50 of the difference between the total of the Prices (target) and the Price for Work Done to Date (Defined Cost)	*Subcontractor's share* 50/50 of the difference between the total of the Prices (target) and the Price for Work Done to Date (Defined Cost) Subcontractor's share 50% of under or overspend
	£
Total of the Prices (target cost) £ 220,000.00	Total of the Prices (target cost) 200,000.00
(£200,000.00 from Subcontract plus *Subcontract fee percentage* of 10% = £220,000.00)	
Price for Work Done to Date (Defined Cost) 192,500.00	Price for Work Done to Date (Defined Cost) 150,000.00
(£175,000.00 from Subcontract plus *Subcontract fee percentage* of 10% = £192,500)	
Difference (saving) (A) 27,500.00	Difference (saving) (A) 50,000.00
Calculation for the Actual Cost £	**Calculation for the Actual Cost** £
Price for Work Done to Date (Defined Cost) 192,500.00	Price for Work Done to Date (Defined Cost) 150,000.00
Contractor's share (Difference between total of the Prices and the Price for Work Done to Date) from (A) above 27,500.00 × 50% 13,750.00	*Contractor's share* (Difference between total of the Prices and the Price for Work Done to Date) from (A) above 50,000 × 50% 25,000.00
Total paid to Contractor = £ 206,250.00 (by *Employer* to *Contractor*)	**Total paid to Subcontractor =** £ 175,000.00 (by *Contractor* to *Subcontractor*)

Note: Subcontractor's total of the prices (target cost) is used in the *Contractor's* build for the total of the prices (target cost).

Index

Terms in *italics* are identified in Contract data and defined terms have capital initial letters.
Page numbers in *italics* refer to diagrams or illustrations.